How to Stay Sober Program Facilitator's Manual

Dr. Emmanuel Nzuzu PhD, MSc, MS, LMHC, CAP

Absolute Author
Publishing House

How to Stay Sober Program: Facilitator's Manual
Copyright © 2022 Dr. Emmanuel Nzuzu
ALL RIGHTS RESERVED

Publisher: Absolute Author Publishing House
Publishing Editor: Dr. Melissa Caudle
Photographs: All photos from Stock Nation and Used with Permission
Cover Designer: https://www.fiverr.com/mahmuddidar

Library of Congress Catalogue-in-Publication Data

How to Stay Sober Program: Facilitator's Manual/ Dr. Emmanuel Nzuzu

p. cm.

ISBN: 978-1-64953-386-9

1. Addiction   2. Self-help   3. Resources

Printed in the United States of America

Table of Contents

Introduction

This manual is designed to enable counselors in alcohol and drug treatment centers to have a broader and deeper understanding of the *How to Stay Sober* model of recovery and be able to present the program to clients clearly and effectively; hereafter referred to as HTSS. The manual by Dr. Emmanuel Nzuzu is to be used together with the book and workbook listed below:

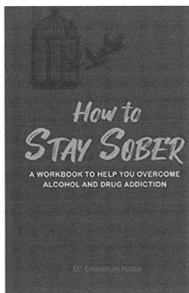

Book: *How to Stay Sober*
A Practical Guide to Overcoming Alcoholism and Drug Addiction

Workbook: *How to Stay Sober*
A Workbook to Help You Overcome Alcohol and Drug Addiction

By the time alcoholics/drug addicts look for help, they would have tried everything possible to solve the problem with little or no success. They are looking for a solution and are desperate for a way out. Anyone can stop using for some time, but such sobriety episodes are short-lived. The challenge is how to stay sober. Alcoholics and drug addicts often look outside instead of going within. They look for what is wrong on the outside in things, other people, and places but often experience failure accompanied by anger, frustration, blaming others, and feeling like victims. HTSS assists them in going within for accurate identification of the problem. The program helps them to focus on healing from the inside-out by a dynamic process of self-diagnosis and making a decision to be guided by a vision of the future and not memories of the past. It enables them to take their power back from alcohol, drugs, other people, and the past. The program encourages participants to be actively engaged in the recovery process instead of passive recovery services recipients.

Unique Features of the HTSS Program
How It Works and Why?

How to Stay Sober Program was developed from years of research, observations, and interactions with alcoholics and drug addicts in different recovery settings. Some settings were psychiatric hospitals, substance abuse treatment programs, dual diagnosis mental health facilities, Alcoholics Anonymous and Narcotics anonymous, prisons and community services help centers and private for-profit providers of substance abuse recovery services.

Below is a list and description of the unique features of HTSS, how it works, and why.

1. Module 1 lays the foundation for successful recovery. Sobriety success is measured not just by the number of accumulated sober days but by progress in changing in beliefs, thinking, feelings, and behavior. Being sober without change inside will lead to relapse.

These desirable changes are achievable through the development of several key strategies, and these are:

   a)   Developing a strong motivation for sobriety just as strong
        as the motivation to use alcohol and drugs.
   b)   Need for rigorous honesty to replace self-deception and
        dishonesty.
   c)   Developing a clear vision of life after alcohol and drugs.
        Participants learn to be guided by a vision of the future and not
        memories of the past.
   d)   Matching desire, expectation, and belief with a vision of sober life.

2. Tools for recovery success used in this program are:

   a) Daily intention

b) Attention
c) Focus
d) Concentration
e) Aggressiveness
f) Consistency
g) Persistency

Desire, Expectation and Belief

Other tools to be integrated into the recovery work are desire, expectation, and belief. Alcoholics and drug addicts display a strong desire to do what they want to do, a greater expectation of experiencing what they want to experience, and a strong belief that they will get what they want.

The facilitator's role is to assist the client in matching their desires with expectation and belief that they can live a life (FREE) from alcohol and drugs. This is a very important aspect of recovery, considering that most alcoholics are fearful, hopeless, helpless, and expect to fail again.

Helping them to raise their desire, expectation, and belief for sobriety can be a sure game-changer.

3. One of the key elements of this program is the opportunity for self-diagnosis (SD). SD is a powerful and effective way for an alcoholic/addict to be persuaded and get convinced that the problem is inside and not outside. SD equips addicts with the skills to take ownership of the diagnosis they do on themselves compared to the diagnosis given to them by family members, their communities, or therapists. SD empowers the addict to desire to take urgent action immediately, to change now rather than later. SD enables the addict to shift from blaming to taking responsibility for all past misbehavior and irresponsible actions.

4. The fourth key strength of the program is that it teaches participants to harness the power of believing. What you believe can work for you or against you. The program defines believing in the following manner:

To believe is to:

✓ To rely on alcohol/drugs or higher power or self
✓ To depend on alcohol/drugs or higher power or self
✓ To trust in alcohol/drugs or higher power or self
✓ To have confidence in alcohol/drugs or higher power or self

Believing creates a relationship between you and that which you believe. Alcoholics have a strong bond with alcohol. Drug addicts have a strong relationship with drugs. One has to believe in a power that delivers you from the bondage of alcohol and drugs. People need wisdom and intelligence to solve problems. Alcohol and drugs have failed to help the alcoholic and drug addict to solve their problem.

The addict's natural wisdom and intelligence have not been able to help him stay sober; there is, therefore, a need to believe in greater wisdom and a higher intelligence.

Success or failure depends on what you come to believe in.

Program participants have a choice.

5. Traditional recovery models emphasize medication above change in thinking, believing, feelings and behavior,

Medication heals the body but does not get rid of self-deception. Medication neither does not automatically make one more honest and trustworthy, nor does medication make an addict more patient, tolerant, considerate, and humble. Long-term sobriety must be anchored in rigorous honesty, patience, humility, love, selflessness, and trustworthiness. *How to Stay Sober* program helps participants to develop and grow in these desirable characteristics.

6. Another strength of the program is Action Planning done during the last two to three weeks before completing the program. Common discharge planning practices in traditional recovery models consist of the following features "Go home, Take your meds, Keep doctors' appointments, look for shelter, look for a job, attend AA meetings, hook up with a sponsor and stay out of trouble." Recovery is an inside job. Action Planning enables participants to create a safe and structured environment to continue sobriety work with more emphasis on the internal factors.

7. This Facilitators' guide is designed to help you in assisting clients to fully understand and embrace the reality of what they have been doing and the gravity of the problem.

When drinking and doing drugs, addicts do not fully grasp that they are engaging in insanity, self-deception, selfishness, self- centeredness, self-abuse, suicidal and homicidal behavior—drinking and getting sick in the morning, regretting every time but doing it again and again is insanity. Drinking into black out or until one passes out is being suicidal. Drinking and driving are homicidal and attempted murder.

Isolating while making alcohol and drugs the priority over loved ones and pushing them away is a serious abuse of family and friends. In this program, alcoholics and addicts should be able to understand and embrace this truth without the feelings of being accused, judged, or criticized. In this regard, the facilitator's role is to clearly guide the client to understand that alcoholism and drug addiction were supported and sustained by self-deception, dishonesty, untrustworthiness, selfishness, and self-centeredness. Self-deception does not allow a person to see through the veil of self-abuse, self-harm, and self-defeating habits associated with alcohol and drugs.

8. Traditional recovery models emphasize abstinence be achieved by avoiding people, places, and things. The alcoholic and drug addict needs to get into a new environment by avoiding people, places, and things. However, avoidance alone does not take the addict far enough if such avoidance is not accompanied by a change in beliefs and thought patterns. The facilitator should assist clients in developing and becoming stronger in the characteristics of rigorous honesty and trustworthiness.

9. Being guided by a vision of the future and not memories of the past. The facilitator's role here is to help clients to prepare for a new life free from alcohol and drugs using the HTSS model. Most clients are used to a life of drinking, drug abuse, and nothing else. Sobriety is dull, tedious, unexciting, and uneventful when compared to the life of alcohol and drugs. They tend to preoccupy their time talking about the problem, how they have lost everything, how hard life is, how bad the situation is becoming. The hopelessness and despair get worse when they no longer drink and do drugs.

They focus more on the horrors they went through instead of concentrating on the new life of sobriety. They continue to live in the past mentally and emotionally, even if they have been clean and sober for some time. Lives guided by memories of the past instead of a vision of the future do not lead to sober living. The facilitator's role is to guide clients in developing and pursuing a vision of the future, a vision of life after alcohol and drugs, something to look forward to and aspire to. A vision that inspires and excites them to move forward with anticipation and expectation.

10. A major challenge for recovery programs is participants' motivation strength, which affects the addicts' commitment level and successful completion rate. Using alcohol and drugs was so effective and successful because of a very strong motivation and high commitment to using daily. Successful recovery demands for an equally strong motivation and commitment to stay sober day after day. HTSS is designed to enable participants, under the facilitator's guidance, to identify their true underlying reasons for quitting alcohol and drugs as opposed to fake, shallow, artificial, and flimsy excuses often given by alcoholics and drug addicts in recovery. A common flimsy reason is doing recovery for the children, spouse, or other family members. These loved ones were always there when the addict was deep in addiction. Why does the addict think that all of a sudden, they love and care for them so much that they are now willing to give up alcohol and drugs for them? Self-deception might have worked when they were using it, but it won't help them get sober. The addict was not drinking and abusing drugs for anyone else's benefit except himself. The role of the Facilitator in this regard is to assist the participant in identifying a strong motivation for sobriety with emotional and psychological content. The identified motivator should compel and inspire the addict into a persistent and consistent change in thinking and behavior necessary for the successful completion of the program.

Session Topics and Learning Objectives

Module A: Recovery Is Possible and Always Available

By the end of this How to Stay Sober program, participants should be able to list, describe, explain, and apply the alcohol and drug addiction concepts and principles covered in these sessions.

Session 1- Recovery Is Possible and Always Available- Session Objectives

- ✓ Be able to list and describe what is recovery?
- ✓ Identify and list at least three to five reasons your previous recovery efforts had limited success.

Session 1 Self-Assessment Quizzes/Exercises/Questions

Session 2 - What Is Your Motivation to Quit Alcohol and Drugs Now?- Session Objectives

- ✓ Be able to describe and explain the definition and meaning of the term motivation.
- ✓ Given a practical exercise, be able to list and describe your own motivation to give up alcohol and drugs now.

Session 2 - Self-Assessment Quizzes/Exercises/Questions

Session 3 - What Is Intention? -Session Objectives

- ✓ Be able to describe and explain the definition and meaning of intention.
- ✓ Be able to describe and explain why it is important to have a clear daily intention for your sobriety.
- ✓ Given a practical exercise, be able to list and describe your own daily intention about staying sober.

Session 3 Self-Assessment Quizzes/Exercises/Questions

Session 4 - What is a Vision?- Session Objectives

✓ Be able to list and describe the definition and meaning of vision.
✓ Be able to describe and explain why it is important to have a clear vision of life after alcohol and drugs.
✓ Given a practical exercise, be able to list and describe your own specific vision for sober living.

Session 4 Self-Assessment Quizzes/Exercises/Question

Session 5 - Future vs Past Orientation- Session Objectives

✓ Be able to describe and explain the difference between future and past orientation.
✓ Given a practical exercise list and describe three things you can do to stop living in the past.

Session 5 - Self-Assessment Quizzes/Exercises/Questions

Session 6 - Need for Rigorous Honesty- Session Objectives

✓ Be able to list and describe the definition and meaning of rigorous honesty.
✓ Given a practical exercise list and describe why you should be rigorously honest with yourself.

Session 6 – Self-Assessment Quizzes/Exercises/Questions

Module B: Self-Diagnosis-How to Accurately Identify the Problem of Addiction to Alcohol and Drugs

Session 1 – Self-diagnosis – Do I have a problem? & What is the problem? - Session Objectives

✓ Be able to describe and explain how to accurately identify the problem of addiction to alcohol and drugs.
✓ Be able to list, describe, and explain why it is important to ask and answer the following question: Do I have a problem with alcohol and drugs?

Session 1 - Self-Assessment Quizzes/Exercises/Questions

Session 2 - Signs and Symptoms of Your Problem with Alcohol and Drugs - Session Objectives

✓ Be able to list and describe the definition of signs and symptoms.
✓ Given a practical exercise list and describe the specific signs and symptoms of the problem that you experienced while using alcohol and drugs.

Session 2 Self-Assessment Quizzes/Exercises/Questions

Session 3 - The Phenomenon of Craving -Session Objectives

✓ Be able to list and describe the definition and meaning of the term craving.
✓ Given a practical exercise, list and describe the specific incidents where you experienced the phenomenon of craving while using alcohol and drugs.

Session 3 Self-Assessment Quizzes/Exercises/Questions

Session 4 - Normal vs Abnormal Drinkers- Session Objectives

✓ Be able to list and describe the difference between normal and abnormal drinkers.
✓ Given a practical exercise, list and describe two incidents from the time you were using, which demonstrate that you are an abnormal drinker/drug abuser.

Session 4 Self-Assessment Quizzes/Exercises/Questions

Session 5 Mental Obsession-Session Objectives

✓ Be able to list and describe the definition and meaning of the term mental obsession.
✓ Given a practical exercise, list and describe two incidents in which you experienced mental obsession after you decided to quit alcohol and drugs. Explain the outcomes of those experiences.

Session 5 - Self-Assessment Quizzes/Exercises/Questions

Session 6 - Admit the Problem-Session Objectives

✓ Be able to list, describe and explain why it is important to ask and answer the following question -- What is the problem with alcohol and drugs?
✓ Be able to list and describe the definition and meaning of the term "to admit."
✓ Be able to list and describe the definition and meaning of "powerlessness."
✓ List and describe five specific ways you were powerless over alcohol and drugs.

Session 6 - Self-Assessment Quizzes/Exercises/Questions

Module C: More About the Problem: Consequences of Powerlessness

Session 1 - Consequences of Powerlessness-Session Objectives

✓ Be able to list and describe the specific ways in which your life was unmanageable due to powerlessness in the following important aspects:

    a) Your Physical Health, Your Mental Health, Your Spiritual health and Your Financial Health
    b) Your Relationship with Yourself, Relationship with Your Family /Friends and Your Marriage(s)
    c) Your Work/Job-Career Life Your legal Life

d) Your Transportation Status and Your Housing/Accommodation
e) Your Hobbies

Session 1 Self-Assessment Quizzes/Exercises/Questions

Session 2 - Lost Love, Respect and Trust- Session Objectives

✓ Given a practical exercise, list and describe the specific things you did to lose the love, respect, and trust of your loved ones.
✓ Given a practical exercise, list and describe the specific things you are going to do to regain lost love, respect, and trust of your loved ones. (What others think and believe about you).

Session 2 Self-Assessment Quizzes/Exercises/Questions

Session 3 - Rebuilding Broken Relationships and Regaining Your Honor, Dignity and Integrity-Session Objectives

✓ Given a practical exercise, list and describe the specific things you will do to regain lost dignity, honor, integrity, and self-worth. (What you think and believe about yourself).

Session 3 Self-Assessment Quizzes/Exercises/Questions

Session 4 - Importance and Benefits of Admitting Powerlessness-Session Objectives

✓ Be able to list and describe the importance and benefits of admitting powerlessness over alcohol and drugs.
✓ Given a practical exercise, list and describe specific aspects that are critical parts to admitting that you are powerless over alcohol and drugs.

Session 4 Self-Assessment Quizzes/Exercises/Questions

Module D: The Solution: Power of Believing

Session 1 - What are Beliefs, and Where do They Come from?- Session Objectives

✓ Be able to list and describe what beliefs are.
✓ Be able to explain where beliefs come from.
✓ Given a practical exercise, list and describe your beliefs about alcohol and drugs when you were using.
✓ Given a practical exercise, list and describe your new beliefs about alcohol and drugs that will help you to stay sober.

Session 1 Self-Assessment Quizzes/Exercises/Questions

Session 2 - Nature of Believing: Spiritual Vs Physical or Non Spiritual-Session Objectives

- ✓ Be able to list and describe the term Spiritual.
- ✓ Be able to list and describe the term Higher Power/God.
- ✓ Given a practical exercise, describe and explain the advantages and benefits of believing in a Higher Power/God as compared to your limited five senses.

Session 2 Self-Assessment Quizzes/Exercises/Questions

Session 3 - Predominant and Recurrent Beliefs of the Alcoholic and Drug Addict-Session Objectives

- ✓ Given a practical exercise, list and describe 10 of your predominant and recurrent beliefs about alcohol and drugs when you were using.
- ✓ Be able to list and describe the term paradigm shift.
- ✓ Be able to list and describe the term emotional addictions.
- ✓ Be able to list and describe the term mind-body-spirit connection.

Session 3 Self-Assessment Quizzes/Exercises/Questions

Session 4 - Restoration to Sanity-Session Objectives

- ✓ Be able to list and describe the term insanity in the context of your addiction to alcohol and drugs.
- ✓ Given a practical exercise, list and describe five specific incidents of insane choices and behavior when you were drinking and using drugs.

Session 4 Self-Assessment Quizzes/Exercises/Questions

Module E: Breaking the Habit of Being Yourself

Session 1 - The Role of Self on Your Way to the Bottom-Session Objectives

- ✓ Be able to list and describe the definition and meaning of the term self-will in the context of addiction and recovery.
- ✓ Given a practical exercise, describe and explain the different components that make up your will and life.
- ✓ Given a practical exercise, describe and explain why you have to give up self-will as a requirement for long-term sobriety.
- ✓ Given practical exercises, list and describe what you get back in return for giving up your self-will.

Session 1 Self-Assessment Quizzes/Exercises/Questions

Session 2 - Self-Will Has Failed: Self-Will Did Not Work-Session Objectives

- ✓ Given a practical exercise, describe and explain why Self-will and Self-Knowledge, on their own, could not help you to stay sober.

Session 2 Self-Assessment Quizzes/Exercises/Questions

Session 3 - Decision Making, Turning Point-Session Objectives

- ✓ Be able to list and describe the definition and meaning of the term decision-making.
- ✓ Given a practical exercise, describe and explain how you arrived at decisions of drinking alcohol and using drugs.

Session 3 Self-Assessment Quizzes/Exercises/Questions

Session 4 - Who Are You Turning To (Spirituality Vs Religion)-Session Objectives

- ✓ Be able to list and describe the difference between spirituality and religion.
- ✓ Given a practical exercise, describe and explain the importance of surrendering to Higher Power/God.

Session 4 Self-Assessment Quizzes/Exercises/Questions

Session 5 - How to Be Under the Influence and Direction of Your Higher Power/God-Session Objectives

- ✓ Given a practical exercise, describe and explain specific ways to put yourself under the influence and direction of your Higher Power/God.
- ✓ Given a practical exercise, list and describe practical ways of developing and cultivating a close relationship with your Higher Power/God.

Session 5 Self-Assessment Quizzes/Exercises/Questions

Module A: Recovery Is Possible and Always Available

Session 1

Numerous failed efforts.

Bottom of the Bottom.

> *"I don't know why I keep doing this to myself. I have tried everything, and nothing has worked so far. I was sober for a period of time but made a mistake and relapsed. I don't want to die. My loved one doesn't trust me anymore. I am lonely, isolated, and alone. I don't know what to do. I need help."*

Believe that they have tried everything, but nothing works.

Main Ingredients for Sobriety

Clear Motivation, Rigorous Honest, Vision and Daily Intention.

What is to recover?

- ✓ Getting back.
- ✓ Restoration.
- ✓ Being rescued from yourself.
- ✓ Repairing broken relationships.

SESSION ASSESSMENT

List and describe at least three reasons why your previous recovery efforts had limited success.

1. _____

2. _____

3. _____

Session 2: What is Your Motivation to Quit Alcohol and Drugs Now?
-Session Objectives: PGS. 2-7 HTSS

✓ Be able to describe and explain the definition and meaning of the term motivation.
✓ Given a practical exercise, be able to list and describe your own motivation to give up alcohol and drugs now.

Motivation for Sobriety

What was your motivation to drink alcohol and use drugs?

Why were you so effective in addiction?

Success in any area of life requires motivation and a certain level of commitment.

You became an expert at drinking and drug abuse because you had a strong motivation to do it.

Your parents, spouse, employer, friends, teachers, church group, couldn't make you quit. You excelled in using alcohol and drugs because you had motivation and commitment.

How strong was your motivation to use?

Your strong motivation prompted you to go and get a drink or a drug.

You thought about it every day, felt it, tasted it, smelled it, and promptly acted on your thoughts.

Identifying your true underlying reasons for quitting alcohol and drugs will propel you to action. Your addiction to alcohol and drugs worked so well because you had your own strong reasons to indulge in them daily.

What is your real reason to do sober life?

How strong is that reason for you to change?

What is your motivation to quit using now and not some other time?

What is your motivation to stay sober?

Successful recovery demands that you identify your genuine reasons to want it. What is the valid and strong reason that makes you want to quit? Any fake, shallow, and artificial excuses will not help you. You may say that you want sobriety for your children, spouse, or other family members. Your loved ones were always there when you were deep in addiction. Why do you think all of a sudden you love and care for them so much that you are now willing to give up alcohol and drugs for them? Self-deception might have worked when you were abusing alcohol and drugs, but it won't help you to stay sober.

How does your motivation to stay sober compare with your motivation to use?

You have to find a good solid, and lasting reason to want to stay sober.

- ✓ Powerful enough to force you into action.
- ✓ Psychological/emotional content.
- ✓ Your reasons to drink and abuse drugs were steeped in emotions and often so strong and powerful that nothing could stop you once you decided to be on them. You got impatient, and nothing could stand in your way.
- ✓ When you wanted a drink and a drug, you would make sure you had them no matter the odds. You were emotional and passionate about your drugs and alcohol.
- ✓ How emotional and excited are you about being sober?
- ✓ What is the driving force behind your sobriety efforts?
- ✓ Your personal reason to quit should inspire you to take a determined effort toward an alcohol and drug-free life.
- ✓ What is it inside you that would motivate you to want sober living and not just daydream about it?

Weak Motivators

> *"I'm not a real alcoholic. I just want to give my body some rest and I can continue anytime, that family members are the problem. All you need is to stop for some time to silence them, that your life would be better if people stopped bothering you about your drinking or that all you need is to slow down then go back to drinking and drug abuse after a short period of recovery."*

When Asked Why Are You in Recovery?

"I don't know for sure. The fact that I am here means that I need it."

Others may say they are in recovery because "My life, I am the problem; I need help." Such responses are too general and meaningless and do not inspire you to take action.

These responses are usually accompanied by disempowering questions such as, "I don't know why I am doing this to myself. I have tried everything, and nothing works. I don't know what to do to stop. I need help, but I am not sure." These may sound like nice logical things to say, but they don't motivate you to move forward. Your reason for making a recovery should prompt you into action.

Practical Exercise 1
What is Your Motivation?

- ✓ Doing recovery for your own personal reasons seems to hold more significant promise in the long term.
- ✓ What do you benefit from sobriety?
- ✓ What is the attraction of quitting alcohol now?
- ✓ What does sobriety mean to you emotionally and psychologically?
- ✓ What does it feel like to be finally free from alcohol and drugs?
- ✓ What is in it for you?
- ✓ What is the benefit for you in a new life of sobriety compared to your old lifestyle?
- ✓ Why should you change now and not later?
- ✓ How much longer are you willing to put up with what you go through when you drink and do drugs?
- ✓ How much longer are you willing to continue investing your life (time and money) in a loss-making enterprise called addiction?

Session 3 - What Is Intention? Session Objectives: P 7-15 HTSS

- ✓ Be able to describe and explain the definition and meaning of intention.
- ✓ Be able to describe and explain why it is important to have a clear daily intention for your sobriety.
- ✓ Given a practical exercise, be able to list and describe your own daily intention about staying sober.

Session 4 - What Is a Vision? Session Objectives: PGS. 2-7 HTSS

- ✓ Be able to list and describe the definition and meaning of vision.
- ✓ Be able to describe and explain why it is important to have a clear vision of life after alcohol and drugs.
- ✓ Given a practical exercise, be able to list and describe your own specific vision

for sober living.

Session 3 and 4 Material

What Is Your Intention and Vision?

"Where there is no vision, the people perish…" (Prov 29:18)

Addiction life is characterized as:

- ✓ Vicious cycle reproducing the same unwanted experiences.
- ✓ Kept thinking in ways that kept you stranded in alcoholism/drugs.
- ✓ Behaved in ways that strengthened your addiction habits.
- ✓ Made choices that led to the same pitfalls and regrets.
- ✓ Engaged in self-defeating thought patterns and beliefs---then wondered why your life was not improving.
- ✓ You walked in the same mental and dreary emotional paths,
- ✓ Falling in the same ditches again without being roused - from the slumber.
- ✓ Puzzled why things were not working out for you, especially where alcohol and drugs were involved.
- ✓ The more you tried, the worse you fell.
- ✓ Lived in anticipation of more hardships because you couldn't move out of Point "A."

How Do You Get Out of Point "A" To "B"?

A-Addiction Life

All things going wrong, it's so hard, nothing works, it's impossible, have tried and failed, don't care anymore, another drink would make you feel better. Spend time crying about the problem; how bad your situation is? Everyone doesn't understand you.

How different and unique is your case? Self-pity, feeling sorry for yourself, and nothing more.

B- NewLife

Focus on answers and solutions

What is your vision of life free from alcohol and drugs?

What is Your Vision? (Where are you now, and where do you want to go?)

Point A

How many years have you been at Point "A"? What do you say to yourself about being at Point "A" for so long?

What do other people say to you about your addiction lifestyle? What and how do you respond to what they say?

What have you tried to do so far in order to get out? How well have your recovery attempts worked so far?

What is keeping you stuck in Point "A"?

Point B

Your vision is your Point "B." It is your desired future life without alcohol/drugs.

Experience desired future life in the present moment. See yourself having successfully recovered.

What is successful recovery for you? What is your life going to be like when you are clean and sober?

How do you think, feel and act now that you are free from alcohol? (Recall what you said to yourself at the height of your addiction).

Having changed successfully, how would you relate and talk to others? How do you want to be perceived?

Session 5 - What is intention? Why it is important to have one?

Intention is knowing what you want and getting clear of what you want to do, have, and be.

Your intent is like a plan, an idea of what you will do and attain. It should be obvious and unmistakable to you. Intention is a resolve, a determination of what you want from recovery, and it should direct your perceptions, choices, and actions.

If you are intent on doing something, you are willing and determined to get it done, you have a burning desire to do it and complete it, you have a firm belief that you can do it and achieve it, you have high expectations of your ability to do it and experience the results in an instant.

Intention helps you to stay on task until the end, to stay focused and not allowing outside distractions to derail your progress. You leave no stone unturned until you get what you want.

Intending Process—5 Parts (Read PGS. 10-15 HTSS)

- ✓ Clear intent
- ✓ Strong desire + Great expectation + Strong belief
- ✓ Attention
- ✓ Elevated emotions
- ✓ Inspired action

Session 6 - Past vs Future Orientation Stop Living in The Past

Intention is very powerful. You drank alcohol and used drugs by intention. Every time you went to drink and pass out intention was there with you.

Your intention was to experience the same sense of ease and comfort that alcohol gave you in previous days. Your intention was to chase the high that cocaine always delivered. Your intention was to numb the painful feelings, a vital service that alcohol always provided on demand.

Your intentions were always past and not future-oriented. You wanted to drink today and feel the way it felt like yesterday. You were using yesterdays' experiences as a reference point for dealing with today's circumstances and challenges.

You repeated past drinking behaviors because that is what you got used to, the familiar, the known, which looks natural, real, and more like who you are being.

Future Orientation

In order to effectively change, your intentions should have a future orientation and be in alignment with your vision.

Sobriety is not in what you are used to and feels good. Sober life is in the unknown and unfamiliar; in what feels strange, unreal, and uncomfortable.

Your sober intentions should support and compliment your vision and not contradict it. Your intention should keep you focused on the new life and not the unwanted familiar past where you are coming from.

Your clear intentions should keep you preoccupied with what you want and not what you don't want; what you have and not what you don't have; what you like and not what you don't like.

It's easy for a recovering addict to be consumed by what is wrong; what is not working; how hard things are, how everyone doesn't understand and like you; and blame, blame, blame.

Session 7 - Need for Rigorous Honesty-Session Objectives - (PGS. 16-22 HTSS)

- ✓ Be able to list and describe the definition and meaning of rigorous honesty.
- ✓ Given a practical exercise, list and describe why you should be rigorously honest with yourself.

Honesty is essential for a life free from alcohol and drugs.

Honesty is not just about telling the truth. It is seeing things as they are and not what they appear to be or what you imagine them to be.

Honesty is about what you think, say, and believe about your relationship with alcohol and drugs. What you think and believe can either work for you or against you.

How honest were your thoughts and beliefs about alcohol/drugs when you were using?

Honesty should promote your welfare and that of your loved ones. How well did your alcohol/drug abuse lifestyle promote your interests and those of your loved ones?

Self-Deception and Dishonesty

Predominant daily thought patterns, self-talk content, feelings, and perceptions guide your drinking/drug abuse life.

Dishonesty-believing a lie/living that lie.

It is a double standard; one standard is for your private consumption and another for public display. When you are dishonest, you always worry about what are they are saying about you because you can't tell which version of you people are seeing and interacting with.

When you lie to yourself about who you are being, you live in constant fear of exposure and may need a drink to numb the fear and anxiety aroused by self-deception.

(Read Jingo, Jodak, Brett, Bango PGS. 17-18 HTSS)

Assess your level of honesty when using. There are no right or wrong answers.

- ✓ How honest were you about your drug/drinking lifestyle?
- ✓ What were the things and issues that you were dishonest about?
- ✓ What were the consequences of dishonesty to you first and to other people in your life?
- ✓ What were the financial and emotional consequences of being dishonest?
- ✓ List and describe five things you are going to practice so that you become rigorously honest?

Practical Daily Exercise 2
My Daily Recovery Success Factors

This daily self-reflection tool is designed to assist you in paying continuous attention to your vision and intentions. Please rate yourself on each of the following important daily self-check items on a scale of 1 to 10 (lowest to highest).

Date: _____

Time: _____

Day of the week: _____

1- Today I strongly want to be sober for myself? _____

2- Today I am highly motivated to work on staying sober? _____

3- Today I strongly believe I succeed in staying sober? _____

4- Today I have strong self-confidence in staying sober? _____

5- Today I am very interested in doing all it takes to stay sober? _____

6- Today I will do all that I have to do in order to stay sober? _____

7- Today I am very open and honest about staying sober? _____

8- Today I am very grateful to be sober? _____

9- Today I have great expectations about staying sober? _____

10- Today I am in a very good mood concerning my sobriety? _____

11- Today I have a very positive attitude toward my new life of sobriety?

_____

_____

_____

12 - Which aspects about yourself need some improvement today, and what specifically are you going to do to improve in those aspects:

_____

_____

_____

_____

_____

_____

_____

Module B - Self-Diagnosis - How to Accurately Identify the Problem of Addiction to Alcohol and Drugs

Session 1 - Self Diagnosis - Do I Have a Problem and What is the Problem? - Session Objectives: (PGS. 23-31 HTSS)

- ✓ Be able to describe and explain how to identify the problem of addiction to alcohol and drugs accurately.
- ✓ Be able to list, describe and explain why it is important to ask and answer the following question, "Do I have a problem with alcohol and drugs?

Misunderstanding of the Problem

Alcoholism is a disease, and many people who drink don't believe that they have an illness. It is impossible to treat a disease that you don't think you have.

To the alcoholic, the drinking lifestyle looks very normal. After all, everyone else drinks alcohol; besides, it is legal, although it may sometimes cause you to do illegal things.

Alcohol and drug addictions are the only diseases that a client must make a self-diagnosis.

The problem is that the alcoholic does not know what the problem is, although he claims to know. Just being aware of a problem without taking corrective action is not sufficient.

Persuade self through denial and self-deception: can stop when you want to, or that "I still have a job or I am still married, or I am still paying my mortgage, and I don't sleep under a bridge, or I don't eat from the garbage can, real alcoholics and addicts are homeless. I am not any of these things; therefore, I am not an alcoholic nor drug addict."

Consider self to be functioning alcoholic and falsely believe that there is no serious problem that warrants taking urgent and drastic action. This kind of misguided thinking justifies continuing the abusive and poisonous relationship with alcohol and drugs with severe long-term consequences to the drinker and his family.

Successful recovery requires you to develop a clear, accurate, and correct understanding of the problem of alcohol and drug addiction.

This can be accomplished by asking and answering two simple but critical questions. The first question is, "Do I have a Problem?"

If the answer is yes, you proceed to the second one: What is the problem? If you answer NO to the first question, you may have no business in recovery because you have nothing to recover from.

Continue using even when such behavior creates problems in health, families, finances, legal, work, education, and marriages.

Do I have a problem?

How many years have you been using alcohol and drugs while experiencing problems with such behavior?

What are your good reasons for drinking and abusing drugs when it causes you such problems?

How wise and sane is your habit of continuing to drink and abuse drugs when that created frequent problems for you?

Since when did it become okay to fall in the same ditch again and again and see nothing wrong with it?

How much longer are you willing and prepared to continue drinking and experiencing the same troubles?

How much time and money do you still want to invest in alcohol and drugs.

(Read Gomba, Booster and Bregga (PGS 29-31 HTSS)

Session 2 -Signs and Symptoms of Your Problem with Alcohol and Drugs - Session Objectives: (PGS. 31-35 HTSS)

- ✓ Be able to list and describe the definition of signs and symptoms.
- ✓ Given a practical exercise list and describe the specific signs and symptoms of the problem that you experienced while using alcohol and drugs.

Signs and Symptoms of Your Addiction Problem

Symptoms are not the problem they indicate the existence of an underlying disease.

Dealing with the symptoms only to find that your drinking and drug abuse was getting worse.

Does not eliminate the problem-ending marriage, move to new a city, changing from whisky to wine, using weekends only, etc.

Dwelling on the symptoms is misleading and often makes you think that you don't have a problem. You cannot solve a problem just by treating its symptoms only.

There are many red flags along the road to becoming an alcoholic and drug addict.

Pattern of getting drunk or high today, run into problems today, go back to using the following day, and the next day with more problems.

Even if the symptoms seem obvious, you continue using day after day thinking that today will be different; and that you will be able to drink normally and safely.

Below is a list of some symptoms of the disease:

- ✓ Always exhausted.
- ✓ Being upset when not drinking or doing drugs.
- ✓ Cannot stop using and drinking when desiring to do so.
- ✓ Pre-occupied with alcohol and drugs, unhappy about work, career or life in general.
- ✓ Bank account is always overdrawn -- most times non-existent.
- ✓ Abandon hobbies and other interests in favor of alcohol and drugs.
- ✓ Staying in unhappy and unfulfilling relationships; sometimes unsafe, abusive, and violent. (Read full list PGS. 33-34 HTSS)

Targeted and Focused Self-Diagnosis Process

Most treatment programs tell the alcoholic what is wrong.

The addict may agree with the given diagnosis superficially without acceptance at a deeper subconscious level.

Many addicts are not entirely convinced that they have a problem even when they are in a treatment program.

Self-diagnosis awakens them to the true nature and magnitude of the problem. The process starts with asking the alcoholic some common thought patterns held while using alcohol and drugs.

Daily Thought Patterns

Below are some examples of standard daily thought patterns:

a) "I can stop when I want."
b) "This will be my last one or today is the last day."
c) "I got this under control."
d) "I will never do this again."
e) "I am not hurting anyone," or "No one knows how much I drink."
f) "People should leave me alone -- it's my money; it's my life."
g) "I drink because she talks too much or because he is hot-headed."

Examination and Analysis-Shocking Revelations

Addiction Thinking-Old Life	Sober Thinking-New Life
Believed & meant it	a- Rigorous honesty
a- Self-deception	b- Loving
b- Dishonesty/lying	c- Selfless
c- Selfishness	d- Patience
d- Self-centeredness	e- Humility
e- Inconsiderate	f- Tolerance
f- Untrustworthy	g- Courage
g- Impatient	h- trustworthy
h- Irresponsible	i- Dependable
I- Inconsiderate	j- Reliable

Session 3 - The Phenomenon of Craving-Session Objectives PGS.36-38 HTSS)

✓ Be able to list and describe the definition and meaning of the term craving.
✓ Given a practical exercise, list and describe the specific incidents where you experienced the phenomenon of craving while using alcohol and drugs.

The first drink is key to understanding the nature of the disease of alcoholism. The first drink always triggers the physical desire for subsequent drinks.

Each drink increases the physical urges for more. As the number of drinks increases, your rational mind gets more intoxicated and impaired by alcohol.

More drinks impair your judgment while increasing bodily physical cravings for more alcohol.

One or two drinks are never enough. The alcoholic never gets enough because of the cravings triggered by the first drink. The first drink is the culprit because the physical urges do not occur if you don't take it.

Session 4 - Normal vs Abnormal Drinkers-Session Objectives (PGS. 38-40 HTSS)

✓ Be able to list and describe the difference between normal and abnormal drinkers.
✓ Given a practical exercise, list and describe two incidents from the time you were using, demonstrating that you are an abnormal drinker/drug abuser.

Abnormal Drinkers

- ✓ First drink triggers craving
- ✓ Inability to stop
- ✓ Allergic to alcohol
- ✓ Toxic substance with no nutritional value
- ✓ Body relaxes and feels mellow instead of rejecting
- ✓ Impaired judgment
- ✓ Body takes over control
- ✓ Drink until pass out

Normal

- ✓ Gets first drink
- ✓ May take hours with one drink
- ✓ Body rejects toxic substance, may not finish first drink, leave it on the table.
- ✓ Feel dizzy, sick, nauseated and out of control
- ✓ Mind/judgement intact, still in control
- ✓ Able to stop after 1 or 2 drinks

Session 5 - Mental Obsession Session Objectives (PGS. 40-41, HTSS)

- ✓ Be able to list and describe the definition and meaning of the term mental obsession.
- ✓ Given a practical exercise, list and describe two incidents in which you experienced mental obsession after quitting alcohol and drugs. Explain the outcomes of those experiences.

Sick and tired of being sick and tired.

Forced you to quit -- sober for a period of time, excitement!!!

Getting your life back together.

Sober living dull, boring and not so joyful.

Challenges -- feel restless, discontent, irritable, frustrated... Memory of sense of ease and comfort.

Inner tension -- "Drink and feel better" while the other side says, "Remember you decided to quit and stay sober."

Boredom and misery get stronger/intense. Each day of frustration and unhappiness intensifies the mental obsession, desire to drink gets stronger and out of control.

Finally, you break your promise.

Session 6 Admit the Problem - Session Objectives (PGS. 41-44, HTSS)

- ✓ Be able to list and describe the definition and meaning of the term "powerlessness."
- ✓ Given a practical exercise, list and describe five specific ways in which you were powerless over alcohol and drugs.

Admit the Problem (What is to admit?)

Alcoholic Anonymous (AA): "We admitted that we were powerless over alcohol and that our lives had become unmanageable."

The disease of alcohol can be summed up in this way:

You want to stop, but you cannot because of the craving in the body triggered by the first drink.

You want to quit, but you cannot because of mental obsession.

The conclusion is that "You are powerless over alcohol" because of the craving and the mental obsession.

To acknowledge.

To truly believe you have a problem, to surrender, own up and stop blaming. Take responsibility and accountability for your choices and actions.

To accept and embrace the truth that you were wrong all these years in believing that alcohol and drugs were your good friends.

Allowing the reality to sink in that you have been an abnormal drinker all these years

Accepting that all along, you were pretending that you are okay, all is well; nothing is wrong when everything was wrong.

So-called nice times bankrupted your integrity, dignity, and relationships with yourself and your loved ones.

To admit is to face the truth that you were lying to yourself all these years and saw nothing wrong with it.

Module C - More About the Problem: Consequences of Powerlessness Session Objectives (PGS. 23-31 HTSS)

Session 1 - Consequences of Powerlessness-Session Objectives

✓ Be able to list and describe the specific ways in which your life was unmanageable due to powerlessness in the following essential aspects:

    a) Your Physical Health
    b) Your Mental Health
    c) Your Spiritual health
    d) Your Financial Health
    e) Your Relationship with Yourself
    f) Relationship with Your Family/Friends and your Marriage(s)
    g) Your Work/Job-Career Life
    h) Your legal Life
    i) Your Transportation Status
    j) Your Housing/Accommodation
    k) Your Hobbies

Your Physical Health

In what specific ways was your "Physical Health" unmanageable because of powerlessness over alcohol and drugs?

1- Feeling sick and bad, but you don't care. No eating and no sleep for many days.

2- Getting anxious and sick while waiting for the dealer to deliver heroin- stomach cramps, sweaty, chills but remain undeterred because heroin is your medicine. Even the nauseating sickness is not a problem because your fix is on the way.

3- Hands shaking, dry heaving, feeling sick like hell, dehydrated-not drinking any water etc.

4- Malnourished from drinking too much alcohol on an empty stomach.

5- Numerous visits to emergency rooms for alcohol-drug related ailments-bruises, cuts, gunshot wounds, drug overdose, high blood pressure, fatty liver, withdrawal pains, road accident injuries, etc.

6- Falling down while drunk or high, broken bones.

7- Staggering around and slurred speech.

8- Drinking till you get sick, drink some more next day to feel better, or just spend the whole day sleeping hopelessly and helplessly only waking up to go to the bathroom.

9- Serious health problems but continue using and drinking without caring. Frequent hospitalizations.

10- Gaining weight that you had worked so hard to lose, face looking puffy, swollen, and unattractive.

Your Mental Health

In what specific ways was your "Mental Health" unmanageable because of powerlessness over alcohol and drugs?

1- Extreme personality changes.

2- Isolated, feeling alone, always unhappy, anxious, sad, depressed, suicidal and homicidal.

3- Always worried and fearful that something bad is going to happen.

4- Always quick to descend into anger, rage, irritation, restlessness.

5- Discontent, and agitation.

6- Feeling bad, guilty, shame, scared and insecure—drank some more alcohol to numb.

7- Feeling helpless and hopeless-inability to control or stop drinking and using drugs.

8- Feeling empty inside, no inner peace, no inner strength.

9- Sudden, rapid mood swings, agitated and impatient with kids, spouse, screaming and shouting at them, blaming them for your troubles.

10- Start to drink early in the morning, drinking daily, drinking during work hours, continue drinking after work until early hours in the morning.

Your Spiritual Health

In what specific ways was your "Spiritual Health" unmanageable because of powerlessness over alcohol and drugs?

1- Quit praying or reading the bible. Only pray when in a fix, for help to get out of trouble.

2- Feeling bad, guilty, shame, and fear that you are beyond rescue and God will not forgive you.

3- Beating yourself up for the inability to control your drinking and drug abuse, criticizing yourself and judging yourself harshly, pulling yourself down by drinking more and more, believing you are beyond help.

4- Spiritually and emotionally bankrupt, barren, harsh, dry desert atmosphere. Nothing works for you anymore.

5- More faith in alcohol and drugs than God.

6- Angry with God for the troubles you were going through. Blame Him for your suffering from alcohol and drugs. Accuse Him of letting you down for not saving your marriage, your job, or some other loss you experienced while using alcohol and drugs.

7- Doubt existence of God, fear that God cannot help you anymore, therefore rely on alcohol, depend on alcohol, trust in alcohol, have faith and confidence in alcohol and drugs.

Your Financial Life

In what specific ways was your "Financial Life" unmanageable because of powerlessness over alcohol and drugs?

1- Always running out of money for essentials, all money has gone to drugs or alcohol.

2- Buy cheap junk food or go without.

3- Bills and credit cards go unpaid.

4- Alcohol and drugs are more important than paying bills and buying food.

5- Spending a lot of money that one did not have -- creditors and debt collectors.

6- Regular power cuts, empty refrigerator, empty stomach and empty life.

7- Making up stories, lies to get money.

8- Working very hard to earn money and quickly hand all of it to the drug dealer and liquor store.

9- Pawn valuable possessions and tell lies to cover up.

10- Not working due to alcohol and drug abuse.

Relationship With Yourself

What was the quality of your relationship with yourself when you were drinking alcohol?

How much quality time did you spend with yourself?

Describe your "me time," which is the quality time you had with yourself when using.

In what specific ways was your "Relationship with Yourself" unmanageable because of powerlessness over alcohol and drugs?

1- Don't care about looks, hygiene, and dressing. Neglect showers, grooming.
2- Low self-respect. Low self-esteem. Do not love yourself anymore.
3- Consider yourself valueless, worthless.
4- Very weak, if any, future focus, dim or no future prospects; stagnant, stuck in life. Preoccupied with obtaining the next drink and on how to get through the day.
5- Tolerate discomfort and inconvenience.
6- Hate self, feel like a loser, a chronic failure.
7- Lack of inhibition—go out with anything and be disgusted the following morning.
8- Dishonesty to self and others.
9- Loss of clear personal identity, do not know who you are anymore, and unhappy with what you have become.
10- No longer experiencing normal feelings; if they show up, you suppress them fast with alcohol and drugs. Self-medicate.
11- Feeling so messed up, you begin to think your loved ones would be better off without you.
12- Fear that you might die young from perpetual self-destruction with alcohol and drugs.
13- Feel you are getting old, don't know where you are going next, and have nothing to show for your old age.
14- Consider yourself to be a social drinker or functioning alcoholic but continue to over drink with serious consequences.
15- Neglected basic house chores, dishes pile up, laundry pile up, the house being extremely messy, all visitors no longer welcome to your house.

Session 2 - Lost Love, Respect, and Trust-Session Objective (PGS. 53-61, HTTS)

✓ Given a practical exercise, list and describe the specific things you did to lose the love, respect, and trust of your loved ones.

1- Parade their flaws while ignoring your own deplorable habits and behaviors.
2- Stop calling them, stop answering their calls, cut them off from your world.
3- Not being on time for special family events.
4- Did not value your loved one's feelings and concerns about your using

drugs and alcohol. Paid lip service and nothing more.

5- Lie about your using, manipulate loved ones for money, make them look like they are the reason for your drinking.

6- Stay out drinking and not going to bed with your spouse.

Your Marriage(s)

How was the quality of your marriage(s) when you were drinking alcohol? How much love, trust, respect, and affection was there?

If you are single, don't feel exempt from examining and answering these questions. Instead of marriage, focus on the romantic relationships you had while drinking alcohol.

In what specific ways was your "Marriage Relationship" unmanageable because of powerlessness over alcohol and drugs?

- ✓ Spouse no more trusting, no respect, no intimacy, hurting spouse extremely by your alcohol and drugs. Always arguing, fighting, and frequently calling the police.
- ✓ Spouse always worried about you. Disappointed by your endless lies about where you were, with who, and what you were doing.
- ✓ Kids are always disappointed, angry, and hurting from seeing you passed out, missing their important functions.
- ✓ No valid reason and embarrassing them in front of their friends.
- ✓ Going through a divorce, battling for kids, setting up private investigators on each other to come up with evidence that the other spouse is the bad one, not a suitable parent.
- ✓ Wondering and being fearful about "will we stay together," spouse might leave you any day or has threatened to.
- ✓ Jealous and envious of a happy close relationship between kids and your spouse while you shy away from them, isolate, push them away, concentrating on your alcohol and drugs.
- ✓ Promise spouse to quit but continue to sneak drinks into the home, get caught again, forgiven again, attend AA to silence spouse, then give up after a few meetings accompanied by weak attempts to stay sober. Complain AA doesn't work for you; it's for alcoholics, and you are not one of them.
- ✓ Continue drinking, given a final warning by spouse to either quit using or leave. Don't know what to do. Maybe seek treatment, which you hate so much and therefore discharge yourself before completing the program.
- ✓ Always too high, too drunk, or too tired to spend time with spouse and kids.

Session 3-Rebuilding Broken Relationships and Regaining Your Honor, Dignity and Integrity-Session Objectives (PGS. 61-63, HTSS)

- ✓ Given a practical exercise, list and describe the specific things you are going to do to regain lost love, respect, and trust of your loved ones. (What others think

and believe about you.)
- ✓ Given a practical exercise, list and describe the specific things you will do to restore lost dignity, honor, integrity, and self-worth. (What you think and believe about yourself.)

Make Up Your Own List

- ✓ Become honesty, patient, tolerant, humble and accepting.
- ✓ Do what you say you are going to do. Act on your word, and deliver on your promises to your loved ones.
- ✓ Be open with your family about your recovery and keep them informed about your sobriety work.
- ✓ Be observant, paying attention to, and respecting their rights, interests and welfare.
- ✓ Allow them to be where they are mentally, emotionally and psychologically about you and your past addiction behavior.
- ✓ Practice better time management by being punctual and showing up as expected.

Session 4 - Importance and Benefits of Admitting Powerlessness-Session Objectives (PGS. 68-70, HTSS)

- ✓ Be able to list and describe the importance and benefits of admitting powerlessness over alcohol and drugs.
- ✓ Given a practical exercise, list and describe specific aspects that are critical parts to admitting that you are powerless over alcohol and drugs.

1- The self-analysis you have done so far should have persuaded you to admit that there is a real problem, not an imaginary one, which needs your attention. You also acknowledge that the problem of powerlessness has been there for a long time.

2- To admit is to finally surrender, no more denial, no more pretense, no more blaming, excuses, and no more fabricated justifications.

3- To admit is to stop fighting the disease, stop resisting, give up, and give in.

4- It is to accept that a problem exists that is more powerful than your limited five senses; therefore, you cannot solve it by yourself without a greater power.

What is to admit?

To admit is to yield to the reality that self has failed, your own efforts are not working and that you need something greater and more powerful than yourself. Alcoholics who do self in recovery find it hard to stay sober.

Admission is taking responsibility for your beliefs, choices and actions. Admitting brings you to a position where you emphatically decide that you cannot continue the same way, you are coming up clean and opening up to the reality which has always been there. To admit is to acknowledge the presence of a problem whose existence you denied for a long time. You are finally conceding to the fact that all along you were a slave to alcohol, it has become your master, and it has taken control over your life. You are practically demonstrating that you now know that you have not been in charge, alcohol was and if you continue to drink, you will also continue to be a servant to alcohol. To admit is to surrender defeat, to throw in the towel.

Some specific issues you are admitting are that you pushed away loved ones and let them down again and again, that you were being dishonesty to think that you were in control when in reality alcohol was, that you continued going in the wrong direction with both eyes open, that you knew something was wrong but did very little to nothing about it, drinking and encountering problems but kept going deceiving yourself that it will get better, hurting yourself and others but remained convinced that you drinking harmed nobody.

You admitted that alcohol and drugs were more important than paying bills, buying food, and spending quality time with family. You are admitting that you have a problem that you didn't know how to handle or do something about, that you were imprisoned and hospitalized by alcohol while walking around the streets, that you liked being high but ignored the consequences, that you used anger to silence people and get what you want, force your way through self- engineered predicaments and sometimes to hide the pain inside.

Benefits of Admitting

The good news is that admitting powerlessness is the beginning of getting your power back. By admitting you are making the wise choice of deciding not to continue fighting an ever-losing battle against alcohol and drugs. To admit is tell yourself and mean it that you are no longer willing to invest your time and money in your downfall. You are commanding yourself to stop scoring your own goals and stop opposing yourself. You are moving from delusional thinking and false hopes that things will get better to being in touch with the reality that you have been going in the wrong direction of a one-way street all these years.

Module D - The Solution: Power of Believing

Session 1 - What Are Beliefs and Where Do They Come from- Session Objectives (PGS. 71-72, 76-79, HTSS)

- ✓ Be able to list and describe what beliefs are.
- ✓ Be able to explain where beliefs come from.
- ✓ Given a practical exercise, list and describe your beliefs about alcohol and drugs when you were using.
- ✓ Given a practical exercise, list and describe your new beliefs about alcohol and drugs that will help you to stay sober.

What are beliefs, and where do they come from?

A belief is a thought that you keep on thinking. Beliefs come from thoughts and feelings about any subject, issue, or topic. If you keep thinking the same thoughts and experiencing the same feelings about a subject, that produces a mood. The same mood over a period of time becomes an attitude. Your predominant daily thoughts, feelings, moods, and attitudes combine and become perceptions that become beliefs and habits. There are many sources of beliefs such as your upbringing, your education, your culture, reading materials, mass media.

What were your daily thoughts about alcohol and drugs when you were using?

What should you keep thinking about now that you want to stay sober?

What is believing?

- ✓ To trust in
- ✓ To rely on
- ✓ To depend on
- ✓ To have confidence in something
- ✓ Believing is a force that is always in operation
- ✓ Your beliefs can either work for you or against you.
- ✓ You became powerless because you gave your power to alcohol and drugs.

How so, you may ask? You believed in alcohol; you trusted in it; you relied on it; you depended on it, and you had confidence in it.

You believed so much in alcohol that you gave it your all and your best. Did whatever alcohol told you to do even when you were opposed to it. Sometimes you knew it was not appropriate to drink at that particular point, but you drank anyway because you no longer had the power to say no. How many times did you drink after you had vowed not to do it again?

Session 2 - Nature of Believing: Spiritual Vs Physical (Non Spiritual)-Session Objectives (PGS. 61-63, HTSS)

- ✓ Be able to list and describe the term Spiritual.
- ✓ Be able to list and describe the term Higher Power/God.
- ✓ Given a practical exercise, describe and explain the advantages and benefits of believing in a Higher Power/God as compared to your limited five senses.

Nature of Believing

Spiritual vs Physical (Non Spiritual)

Sense Knowledge Believing

Limited to what you can see, hear, feel, taste and touch.

The known and the familiar self-effort which you have been using to get sober belongs to the limited field of the five senses.

You believed in alcohol/drugs because you could see the beer, smell it, taste it, feel it and drink it.

Believing Beyond 5 Senses

Step 2 of AA: "Came To Believe That A Power Greater Than Ourselves Could Restore Us To Sanity."

The believing espoused in Step 2 is spiritual based on the invisible, non-physical, vast, more powerful and unlimited. It is the realm of the unknown, the unfamiliar; where the impossible becomes possible. It is the field where all potentials and opportunities exist.

What you come to believe implies developing new beliefs to replace the old and limited sense-based beliefs.

Spiritual believing requires you to see the invisible, believe the unbelievable, expect the unexpected, experience and witness the impossible, trust the unknown. This is the realm of the greater power, Higher Power-God.

Believing in a Greater Power

✓   Get help from a source that can deliver you and rescue you all the time and not sometimes. You need wisdom and intelligence to solve problems. Higher power is greater intelligence and greater wisdom.

✓   Higher Power is higher and greater than your limited five senses.

✓   Your five senses are inadequate to overcome alcoholism/drugs.

✓   The more you hold on to your old beliefs about alcohol, the more you stay the same, and relapse will appear soon.

✓   Alcohol helped sometimes; temporary relief with numerous negative side effects.

✓   You sought the help of alcohol and drugs to deal with whatever you were going through but you paid a very heavy price to access that assistance.

✓   How long do you want to continue to rely on what is unreliable?

✓   How long do you want to continue to depend on what is undependable?

✓   How long do you want to continue to trust in what is untrustworthy?

Characteristics and Abilities of God/HigherPower

Higher Power	Alcohol/Drugs
<ul><li>Available 24/7</li><li>Always present wherever you are and whatever you are doing</li><li>Works with you as you are No deals to be made</li><li>No special qualifications needed</li><li>God never goes to sleep or summer vacation; you don't have to pay any dues or stand in a line for your turn No appointments</li><li>No opening hours</li></ul>	<ul><li>Run out or no money Go looking for it</li><li>Possess self-deception and dishonesty</li><li>Make deals, manipulate, hustle</li><li>Selfishness, self-centeredness</li><li>Closed, debts, dangerous, broken promises</li><li>Limited Wisdom</li></ul>

Other important considerations that you should reflect on daily are that Higher Power is:

- Trustworthy
- Reliable
- Dependable
- Honesty
- Powerful
- All-knowing
- All-seeing

- Loving
- Caring
- Kind
- Compassionate
- Present all the time
- Present everywhere

Alcohol and drugs couldn't provide these healing and liberating qualities. You looked to alcohol for inner peace and good life but only got short-lived bliss and a lot of regrets. Believe in something stronger, greater, and more powerful than alcohol and drugs.

Session 3 - Predominant and Recurrent Beliefs of The Alcoholic and Drug Addict-Session Objectives (PGS. 75-90, HTSS)

✓ Given a practical exercise, list and describe 10 of your predominant and recurrent beliefs about alcohol and drugs when you were using.
✓ Be able to list and describe the term paradigm shift.
✓ Be able to list and describe the term emotional addictions.
✓ Be able to list and describe the term mind-body-spirit connection.

Predominant and Recurrent Thought Patterns of the Alcohol and Drug Abuser

✓ Why couldn't I stop drinking?
✓ I tried everything and nothing worked.
✓ I am sick and tired of being sick and tired.
✓ Awareness that continued use means hospital, jail or death.
✓ Human beings create things and experiences from thoughts and feelings.
✓ Success comes from your beliefs, thoughts and feelings so does failure.
✓ Failure thought patterns will not give you success.
✓ Stinking thinking will not give sobriety.
✓ Your failure to stop drinking can be traced to your beliefs, thoughts and feelings.
✓ Become familiar with your own prevalent, continuous and consistent self-deceptive beliefs and thought patterns.
✓ Some common beliefs that alcoholics and drug addicts are usually preoccupied with. (See PGS. 76-79, HTSS)

Paradigm Shift

Some alcoholics get sober but do not work on changing their beliefs and are shocked when they relapse.

Old and new beliefs cannot exist together in harmony because the old ones are stronger, more powerful and ingrained as your habits.

Years of thinking, believing and doing alcohol does not easily go away just because you have decided to be sober.

What is a paradigm?

Paradigms are rigidly established, stubborn and ongoing unwritten rules that direct and govern your behavior. You have an ingrained system of beliefs, ideas, values, attitudes, and habits of seeing the world and behaving.

Social science has established that a part of the growing process involves the acquisition and development of memorized, automatic behaviors and emotional responses that define each individual as a personality.

As a person grows older, 95% of who you are is in a set of memorized programs (in the body and subconscious mind). Overtime, the growing person becomes so familiar with himself so much that automatic (often undesirable) thoughts go by unnoticed.

Emotional Addictions

Automatic emotional reactions and behaviors become part of your personality.

Behind every addiction there are some memorized emotions that drive the addictive behavior such as being hooked up to drugs, alcohol, gambling, sex and shopping.

The process of thinking and feeling the same negative way over many years makes you chronically unhappy, lonely, bored, anxious, depressed, angry, bitter, miserable or physically unwell.

You may begin to use past events in your life to validate and justify your memorized negative emotions that have become part of who you are.

Generally, human beings tend to hide their fears, insecurities, and weaknesses from others. Change becomes a real struggle because you are trying to work out a solution with the same mind that created the problem.

It is almost impossible to solve your problems while you continue to live by emotions of the past. Looking at the bad experience and reliving the event that caused the problem initially will only serve you by re-arousing the old painful emotions, giving a strong reason for you to feel the same negative and painful way.

The framework of mind that created alcohol/drug addiction cannot help you to stay sober.

Unmemorize the self-limiting beliefs and emotions. Freedom comes from confronting your true self and bringing out those fears and weaknesses to your awareness.

Identify and make a list of the negative and self-defeating aspects and replace them with positive, productive beliefs and traits.

Self-observation, awareness and acceptance are the key skills for effective change of self. Observe and become aware of negative emotional states that have had a huge impact on your life.

Identify and recognize aspects of your personality that drive your thoughts and automatic addiction behaviors.

Do constant self-observation and self-awareness so that no emotion, no subconscious behavior or automatic habit goes without your notice.

Mind-Body Connection (PGS. 83-85, HTSS)

Every time you have a thought the brain produces a chemical that immediately sends signals to the body, telling it to feel exactly the same way the mind is thinking.

Great, unlimited happy thoughts produce chemicals that make you feel happy, joyful, uplifted and good.

If you have negative, self-defeating thoughts, you produce chemicals that make you feel bad, down, and unhappy.

If you have an insecure thought, you also begin to feel insecure. If you have fear thoughts, you also start to feel fearful. The moment you feel insecure, you also start to think the way you are feeling, leading to the production of more chemicals to continue to feel the way you are thinking and thinking the way you are feeling. You get caught up in this cycle of thinking and feeling, resulting in feeling becoming the means of thinking.

The mind is now immersed in the body when you think based on how you feel. You are no longer thinking like a mind or conscious being. You are now thinking as the body because the body is determining the outcome based on feelings.

Your perceptions, choices, and behaviors are guided by your feelings and not rational thinking.

How much rational thinking did you put into drinking alcohol?

Your state of being always consists of what you think and how you feel. As your addiction progressed, there came a time when you couldn't think any other way besides the way you felt. You wake up in the morning feeling bad, and you start thinking bad; you feel bad and spend the whole day perceiving things from the way you feel.

The body should be a servant to the mind, but when you think based on how you feel, the mind becomes the servant to the body. Now the body tells you that you need a drink, or it's okay to have a drug.

The moment you begin to feel the way you think because the brain is in constant contact with the body, you begin to think the way you feel and produce more chemicals to feel the way you think and think the way you feel. This cycle of thinking, feeling, and thinking conditions the body to memorize habitual patterns and behaviors better than the conscious mind.

When the brain keeps signaling the body in the same way or with the same messages, the body becomes the mind, and the body knows better than the brain.

How often did you drive and get home alive but cannot remember how you got there? Who drove you home on those occasions when you blacked out while sitting behind the wheel? That is how habits and your behaviors exist.

You may consciously want to change and seriously declare that you want to be sober, but over the years, you have conditioned your body to be unhappy, unhealthy, to be guilty, to be negative, or fearful, and depend on alcohol for relief.

Your conscious mind wants a new life, but your subconscious mind (the body) is used and addicted to the hormones of stress cooled down by alcohol.
When mind and body are working in opposition, there can never be change especially when the body becomes the mind.

Successful change demands that you think greater than how you feel, to think greater than the memorized emotions in the body.

Practical Exercise

Old Beliefs

What did you think, feel and believe about alcohol and drugs when you were using?

Read case histories—*Lonestart, TipsMe, & FixMe (PGS. 81-89, HTSS)*

New Beliefs

What should you think, feel and believe about alcohol and drugs now that you want to stay sober?

Read case histories—*Lonestart, TipsMe, & FixMe (PGS. 81-89, HTSS)*

Session 4 - Restoration to Sanity Session Objectives (PGS. 90-95, HTSS)

✓ Be able to list and describe the term insanity in the context of your addiction to alcohol and drugs.
✓ Given a practical exercise, list and describe five specific incidents of insane choices and behavior when you were drinking and using drugs.

Restoration to Sanity

Step 2 of AA states, "We came to believe that a Power greater than ourselves could restore us to sanity.

What is insanity?

How were you insane when you were doing alcohol and drugs?

Definition--doing the same things over and over, expecting different results.

It is believing a lie and living a lie. Unfortunately, these are lies you tell yourself daily and not somebody else.

A typical way of thinking among alcoholics runs something like this:

> "I am different, alcohol does not affect me like the other people. I am not one of them. They cannot handle their booze. I can enjoy my book more if I smoke a joint. Then I would re-read one page more than five times and give up after several failed attempts. I would do it again the next day hoping it works this time. It never worked and I never completed reading any book."

Question: In what specific ways were you insane while drinking and doing drugs?

Behaviors and habits that are unacceptable and un-cautionable to the rest of society are viewed as normal and standard practice among people who use drugs and alcohol. Here is another example of insanity patterns:

> "I kept telling myself that today I will take the meds as prescribed but always ended up taking double or more sometimes. I used meds for thirty days in less than two weeks. I would agree with family members on the number of drinks but always drank more than agreed. They were unfair to me. I didn't see anything wrong with my alcohol. I told myself that I would clean the house better this time with some alcohol but the house never got cleaned. Every time I completed treatment, I was convinced that now I can control my drug habit and went back to using soon after discharge. It never worked and treatment did work because I was thinking that I can now use safely after treatment."

Module E - Breaking the Habit of Being Yourself

Session 1 - The Role of Self on Your Way to the Bottom-Session Objectives (PGS. 96-100, HTSS)

- ✓ Be able to list and describe the definition and meaning of the term self-will in the context of addiction and recovery.
- ✓ Given a practical exercise, describe and explain the different components which make up your will and your life.
- ✓ Given a practical exercise, describe and explain why you have to give up self-will as a requirement for long term sobriety.
- ✓ Given practical exercises list and describe what you get back in return for giving up your self-will.

The Role of Self on Your Way to the Bottom

Falsely believe you were in control and in charge of your life.

Had given over your will and your life to the care of drugs and alcohol. You were no longer in control, alcohol was.

Several choices:

> a) You can try to change and stay sober depending on yourself (5 senses).
> b) Second choice is to continue depending on alcohol hoping that one day you will be able to drink moderately, and
> c) Third choice is to develop a relationship with and surrender to God-Higher Power.

The choice is yours. There are many people in treatment programs who are struggling to stay sober because they have not made the decision to cut ties with alcohol, hoping that somehow they will be able to control their drinking based on self-knowledge and their own smartness.

What is self, and why do you have to give up self-will?

"I want what I want now irrespective of the costs or consequences." You always drank even when all the odds were stacked against you.

You forced your way on things, situations, and people against their will and interests. The AA-Big Book states that the main source of trouble for the alcoholic is selfishness and self-centeredness and that alcoholics are driven by fear, self-delusion mixed with self-pity to hurt their innocent loved ones without reason forcing them to retaliate.

Most of those choices were made within a framework of selfishness, and self-deception driven by fear, resentment, self-seeking attitude, and pressure for immediate self-gratification.

Life motivated by "I want what I want when I want it" can hardly be successful. It is very mean, egocentric, dishonesty, impatient, intolerant, and impulsive.

Selfishness is the lack of consideration for others.

It is being concerned mainly by one's own personal gain, profit or pleasure at the expense of other people.

A selfish and dishonesty person always places himself in a position to be hurt and be in conflict with himself and others. When things don't go his way he becomes angry, indignant, resentful and blame everyone else except himself.

A self-centered person creates problems for himself and blame other people for the mess. You want the whole world to see how you feel but you do not care about the feelings of others.

Egocentric is inability to view things any other way except your own way. Your way or no way. Such a person has inconsistencies between the standards which apply to himself and those to which he expects others to adhere to.

An egocentric and self-centered person knows the difference between right and wrong but consistently chooses wrong with no hesitation.

A self-centered person is excessively preoccupied with himself and his own needs. It is all about "me, me, me."

Such a person thinks only about himself, his own desires, needs and interests while ignoring those of others especially your loved ones.

A self-seeking person is obsessed with self, self-absorbed, inconsiderate, thoughtless, unthinking and motivated by one's personal advantage without regard for others.

To a self-seeking person, it does not matter how others feel because it's all about you.

A major worry of the selfish person is "when will the rest of the world stop misbehaving and start behaving," so he can be happy.

Self has failed and must be given up or else you continue drinking and doing drugs driven by selfishness, self-centeredness and self-seeking behavior.

He is consumed by his own selfish interests and welfare to the complete disregard of those of others.

Such a person is excessively conceited, preoccupied with his own life and circumstances while being very disinterested in the well-being of others especially your loved ones.

Question: Write a list of actions you knew to be wrong and inappropriate but did it, anyway?

Here are some examples:

- ✓ Used family money on drugs and alcohol instead of bills and food.

- ✓ Stole pain medication from grandma and failed employment drug test.

- ✓ Neglecting to take care of my kids; suffer from lost love and respect but continued drinking alcohol.

- ✓ Ignore family concerns about my alcohol and drug abuse; and hurting them again and again.

- ✓ Offer sexual acts for drugs, feel bad, guilty and shame but do it again, anyway. Unfaithful to spouse, what I wanted was more important than the marriage. Spouse was hurt, furious, angry and disappointed but I didn't care. My drugs were priority. (See PGS. 99-100, HTSS)

What is the Self that you must give up?

Give up dishonesty for honesty, selfishness for selflessness, impatience for patience, untrustworthiness for trust, inconsideration for consideration, self- centeredness for loving, caring and concern for others, from self-seeking to seeking opportunities to be of service in your life and your community.

The fact that you have stopped drugs and alcohol does not automatically make you humble, honest, tolerant and patient. If you have been selfish and self- centered for many years, these negative habits will not go away on their own. They will not disappear just because you have stopped drinking for a few days.

People in recovery usual believe that all they need is to stop drinking and all will be utopia. Being sober is not enough, you have to work at humility, tolerance, patience and honesty. You cannot eliminate selfishness by wishing it away or by using your own power. You need God's help. If you could do it on your own, you would have stopped using and living sober many years back. Have God do for you what you cannot do for yourself.

Question: In what specific ways were you selfish, self-centered and self-seeking when you were doing alcohol and drugs? Describe specific incidents of the manifestation of self and self-will when you were doing alcohol and drugs?

_____

_____

_____

Session 2 - Self-Will Has Failed: Self-Will Did Not Work-Session Objective (PGS. 96-100, HTSS)

Given a practical exercise, describe and explain why self-will and self-Knowledge, on their own, could not help you to stay sober.

What is your will and your life?

- ✓ Your will and your life are given expression in your beliefs, thoughts, choices and behaviors.
- ✓ The will of a person is his thinking, and the life of a person are all his actions put together.
- ✓ Turning "our will and our lives" is saying goodbye to your addictive thought patterns and behaviors. You no longer need them because they were fueling the addiction lifestyle.
- ✓ You need new thinking habits that support sobriety. Examples of self-defeating and self-destructive belief patterns are "I am in control. I got this. It ain't that bad. I can stop when I want". It is not possible to stay sober based on this kind of false and dishonesty thinking.
- ✓ Unfortunately, some people in recovery continue to think the way they are used to and are disappointed when they relapse repeatedly.
- ✓ Step 3 of AA requires you to turn over your will and your life to the care God of your own understanding. You have to become a new person in your thinking, feeling and believing.

Session 3 - Decision Making, Turning Point- Session Objectives (PGS. 101-104, HTSS)

Be able to list and describe the definition and meaning of the term decision-making.

Given a practical exercise, describe and explain how you arrived at decisions of drinking alcohol and using drugs.

The problem is powerlessness and solution is believing in a greater power.

- ✓ Decide where to get the power and how to stay connected to it.
- ✓ You need a power that possess higher intelligence and greater wisdom. A power that will enable you to stop and stay sober.
- ✓ You were always connected to alcohol and drugs all day every day (as your higher power).
- ✓ The power of alcohol and drugs has let you down all these years. Your own power has failed too.
- ✓ This is a major turning point that requires sound decision making. Business as usual will not work.

Decision Making, Turning Point

- ✓ What is decision-making?
- ✓ How did you make decisions when you were using alcohol and drugs?
- ✓ How was the quality of those decisions?

41

✓ How sound were your daily decisions to do alcohol and drugs?
✓ What considerations were those decisions based on?
✓ How proud and satisfied are you about those decisions then and now?
✓ How smart and wise do you look?
(Read PGS. 101-104, HTSS)

Session 4 - Who Are You Turning To (Spirituality Vs Religion)-Session Objective (PGS. 105-107, HTSS)

Be able to list and describe the difference between spirituality and religion.

Given a practical exercise, describe and explain the importance of surrendering to Higher Power/God.

✓ How do you feel about letting go off habits that you have been practicing for many years?

✓ How do you feel about allowing someone or something to exercise control over your life? (Alcohol and drugs were controlling you.)

✓ People ask, "How can a God I don't see and understand help me to stop drinking and stay sober?" In their desperation, they create imaginary Higher Powers who are both physical and visible. They forget that they were already using alcohol and drugs as their Higher Power/God

Stories abound where people have used their dog, a tree, a friend or chair as their Higher Power.

What is religion?

Spirituality is not the same as being religious. Religion is about strict adherence to beliefs, rules, regulations and procedures. It is a normal way of doing things following accepted standards. People born in different religions are raised and expected to respect and obey their religious customs and teachings without question. Such beliefs and expectations are from outside the person. On the other hand, spirituality is from within.

What is spirituality?

Every person is spiritual and not necessarily religious.

Believing in something greater than yourself.

Need for someone/thing to trust in, to rely on, to depend on and to have confidence in. Something with higher intelligence and greater wisdom than your 5 senses.

Spiritual life starts with surrendering whereby you admit being helpless and that you simply don't know how to resolve the situation. If you did, you would have been sober long ago.

All these years you have been turning over your will and your life to untrustworthy, unreliable and erratic power of alcohol and drugs.

Now you are to yield your thoughts and actions to the Source of Life, the Universal Mind, Universal Intelligence, and Infinite Wisdom who is all knowing, all present, all powerful, all loving, compassionate and always forgiving.

You are turning over your life to the Greatest Wisdom, creator and owner of the whole universe, including the natural and supernatural, the physical and non- physical, the visible and invisible, and of the known and unknown.

Higher Power/God is the Divine presence in you, around you, all over you, who works for you, and works with you. God does not reside in some distant place far away from you and beyond your reach. He is always with you; in your past, present and future.

You are turning over your life to the power that keeps you breathing and alive in your sleep. He is the Universal Intelligence that wakes you up every morning and has numbered the hairs on your head. He is the one who helps you to drive your car in the middle of the night while you are very drunk and unconscious.

You made alcohol/drugs your helper and your God.

Most, if not all of your efforts to solve the problem have failed. Now is the time to try something that works.

God is already with you and working in you. How many addicts do you know who are no longer here because of alcohol and drugs? Yet you are still alive. Is it because you are smarter?

He enables your lungs to breathe and your heart to beat. Can you do it with your five senses?

You are to turn over your life to the one who kept you safe and alive during your frequent visits to violent, crime ridden and drug infested neighborhoods. How did you survive the deadly gunfire wars, the dangerous robberies and the self-abuses of your body (not eating food for long periods).

You are giving over your will to the one who always protected you, defended you and loved you; free of charge. You couldn't afford, anyway.

Why surrendering to God-Higher Power is important?

The same mind that created a problem cannot solve the problem.

The thought patterns, beliefs, and memorized emotional responses that produced the addiction cannot be relied on to solve the problem.

Addictive thinking and believing created the alcoholic lifestyle, and that same way of thinking cannot take you to sober living.

Have you ever wondered why your life has not been changing in-spite of the hard work you put into it? The thoughts that you have been thinking have not given you the answer that you have been looking for all these years. The beliefs that you have been believing have not given you the sober life that you desire. The actions that you have been acting have led you downhill instead of uphill. The choices that you have been choosing have consistently led you to a dead end.

How much longer are you prepared to keep getting lost and relapsing?

Here is your opportunity to change by letting go of limited thinking and addiction-oriented beliefs while you surrender to an unlimited, greater, and more resourceful power.

Surrendering gives you immediate access to God's limitless knowledge and bountiful wisdom. It is allowing Him to guide and direct you to sober living.
Read (PGS. 107-114, HTSS)

Session 5 - How to Be Under the Influence and Direction of Your Higher Power/God-Session Objectives (PGS. 116-125)

- ✓ Given a practical exercise, describe and explain specific ways to put yourself under the influence and direction of your Higher Power/God.

- ✓ Given a practical exercise, list and describe practical ways of developing and cultivating a close relationship with you Higher Power/God.

Under The Influence of Alcohol vs Under the Inspiration of God

You are familiar with being under the influence of alcohol and drugs. The question is how to become under the influence and direction of your Higher Power?

Some people object to the idea of giving control over to a Higher Power.

Invisible and Unfamiliar

Higher Power control is hard, impractical, very difficult and sometimes just not acceptable.

- ✓ Who is Higher Power, God?

✓ What is He like?

✓ How do I contact and connect with this invisible power?

✓ How do I work with a power I do not see?

✓ How do I know if God/Higher Power is real?

✓ Resort to using their self-will and own effort hoping for a different result.

✓ Endless pattern of relapses when alcohol is your higher power:

✓ Surrendered your power, authority, independence and freedom to alcohol and drugs.

✓ Although it's all gone, it doesn't look so in your addicted brain.

✓ False belief of being in charge.

Below is proof that you had become a prisoner to alcohol/drugs, a kidnap victim, a servant and a slave.

✓ Thinking about alcohol/drugs all day, every day.
✓ Living in anticipation of the next one.
✓ Confusing alcohol and drugs for a dear friend.
✓ Preoccupied with thoughts of obtaining.
✓ Alcohol/drugs- a major priority above work, family, friends
✓ Putting all your energy into alcohol and drugs.
✓ More excited and enthusiastic about alcohol and drugs.
✓ All your decisions, choices, and activities are dictated by alcohol
✓ Lost direction to alcohol and drugs

Surrendering to a Higher Power should not be difficult because you did it while doing alcohol and drugs.

✓ Regain control by surrendering to Higher Power/God
✓ More helpful and resourceful power
✓ Greater wisdom and intelligence than yourself, greater than alcohol
✓ More powerful than your drug of choice
✓ More reliable than your limited thinking
✓ Possess a lot of practice and experience in surrendering while using
✓ You handed your life over to alcohol and drugs.

How to establish a relationship with God-Higher Power?

What exactly do you do in order to work with a Higher Power/God?

Qualities of successful relationships: Love, trust, respect, honesty, commitment, loyalty, active listening and paying attention, patience, etc.

How addicts viewed their relationship with alcohol/drugs--- characterized by deep love, devotion and commitment. (Read PGS. 120-125, HTSS)

Thought Starters for Discussion and Enhanced Comprehension

These thought starters are to be used as teaching-learning points to generate discussion, debate, increased participation, and engagement of the learners. They can also be used as a checklist to ensure that the major points of each session have been covered thoroughly.

Module A Thought Starters

Definition of Recovery (HTSS PGS. 1-2)

- ✓ What is to recover according to the book?

- ✓ What are some things that an alcoholic and drug addict want to get back by doing recovery work?

- ✓ What does the following phrase mean "being rescued from yourself?"

- ✓ What does the following phrase mean "recovery is restoration of all the intangible assets?

- ✓ What is a "safe and structured environment" for you to do your recovery work?

- ✓ Not drinking alcohol or not doing drugs for some time is not adequate for you to stay sober. What else do you need in order to stay sober? (Suggested Answer—Change from the inside out—beliefs, thoughts, feeling, moods, attitude and perceptions)

What Is Your Motivation to Give Up Alcohol and Drugs? (HTSS PGS. 2-7)

- ✓ Why were you so effective as an alcoholic or drug user?
- ✓ What were your strong reasons for doing alcohol and drugs day after day?
- ✓ Success in any area of life requires motivation and a certain level of commitment. What is motivation and commitment?
- ✓ What are the benefits of a strong motivation to stay sober?
- ✓ What are your real reasons to do sober life? How strong are those reasons for you to change?
- ✓ According to the book, what are some of the fake, shallow and artificial excuses to stay sober given by alcoholics and drug addicts?
- ✓ What are the characteristics of strong motivators? (Suggested Answer: should be clear and specific; have emotional and psychological appeal; should inspire you, excite you, energize you and compel you to take action).

What Is Your Intention and Vision? (HTSS PGS. 7-8)

Changing From Alcoholism to Sober Living Can Be Likened to Transformation from Point "A" To Point "B"

✓ Describe the quality of your life at Point A?

✓ How many years have you been at Point A?

✓ How do you feel about yourself being at Point A for so long?

✓ What do you say to yourself about being at Point A for so long?

✓ Describe your addiction life experiences at Point A?

✓ How long have you been trying to get out of Point A?

✓ What do other people say to you about your addiction lifestyle?

✓ What and how do you respond to what they say?

✓ What have you tried to do so far in order to get out?

✓ How well have your recovery attempts worked so far? What worked; what did not work, and why?

✓ What is keeping you stuck in Point "A"?

Your vision is your Point B (HTSS PGS. 9-10).

✓ It is your desired future life free from alcohol and drugs. It is best to see yourself experiencing that desired future life in the present moment. See yourself in that role of having successfully recovered. Success means different things to different people.

✓ What is a successful recovery for you?

✓ What will your life be like when you are clean and sober?

✓ How do you think, feel and act now that you are free from alcohol and drugs?

✓ What is your new attitude towards yourself and other people important to you?

✓ What would you say to yourself now that you are sober? (Recall what you used to say to yourself at the height of your addiction).

✓ How would you relate and talk to others now that you have successfully changed?

✓ How do you want to be perceived?

What is intention? & Why is it important to have one? (HTSS PGS. 10-14)

1- What are the different ways to describe intention according to the book?
2- What are the benefits of having a clear and specific intention every day?
3- According to the book, what is the difference between past and future orientation?
4- Which orientation is better and why?
5- Write your daily sobriety intentions?

Need for Rigorous Honesty (HTSS PGS. 16-22)

Why is being rigorously honest with yourself essential for a life free from alcohol and drugs?

- ✓ What does the following phrase mean "Recovery is an inside job?"
- ✓ Do you agree or disagree with the following statement: "Honesty or dishonesty is about what you think, say and believe about your relationship with alcohol and drugs?"
- ✓ Why do you agree or disagree?
- ✓ How honesty were you about your drinking lifestyle?
- ✓ What were the things and issues that you were dishonesty about?
- ✓ What were the consequences of being dishonesty to yourself first and to other people in your life?
- ✓ What were the financial and emotional consequences of being dishonesty?
- ✓ Dishonesty is believing a lie and living that lie. What were the double standards that you engaged in when you were using alcohol and drugs?
- ✓ Which version of yourself did you want people to see?
- ✓ Which version of yourself did they actually see and interact with?
- ✓ What does the following statement mean to you? "Your daily self-talk must support your goal to be sober and not contradict it. The thoughts that you hold in your inner self must help you to go in the right direction and to stay on track."
- ✓ List and describe five things you are going to practice so that you become rigorously honest?

Module B Thought Starters
Introduction to Module B (HTSS PGS. 23-25)

- ✓ What is the meaning of the following phrase "Alcoholism is a disease?"

- ✓ How clear, accurate and correct was your understanding of the addiction problem?

- ✓ What was your response when people asked you to seek help or get into an addiction treatment program?

- ✓ What was your attitude and mindset when you attended the very first substance abuse treatment program in your life?

- ✓ Was there a time when you no longer enjoyed using but continued to use, anyway?

✓ How did you justify your behavior of doing something you no longer enjoyed?

✓ What is the meaning of the following phrase "having an abusive and poisonous relationship with alcohol and drugs?"

✓ According to the book, what is the danger of classifying yourself as a functioning alcoholic?

Do I have a Problem with Alcohol? (HTSS PGS. 25-31)

✓ List some of the reasons you should ask and answer the following question, "Do I have a problem"? (Use the textbook for your answer).

✓ Explain the meaning of the following statements "You cannot solve a problem that you cannot describe accurately. You cannot solve a problem that you believe you don't have. You cannot solve a problem whose existence you deny."

✓ According to the book, "When asked, "What is your problem?" addicts seeking help often respond as follows: Alcohol is the problem, drinking too much. My life, my mind, I am the problem. Sleeping is the problem. My job, too much stress." List five of your own explanations of what you believed was the problem when you were using?

✓ How many years have you been using alcohol and drugs while experiencing problems with such behavior?

✓ What were your good reasons for continuing to drink and drug abuse when it caused you such problems?

✓ How wise and sane is your habit of continuing to drink and abuse drugs when that created frequent problems for you?

✓ Since when did it become okay to fall in the same ditch again and again?

✓ How much longer are you willing and prepared to continue drinking and experiencing the same troubles?

✓ How much time and money do you still want to invest in alcohol and drugs?

Signs and Symptoms of Your Problem with Alcohol (HTSS PGS. 31-35)

✓ Many people offer advice and solutions to those who have problems with alcohol and drugs. According to the book what is the fault with those advises and solutions?

✓ What are symptoms? How do the symptoms of alcohol and drug addiction differ from the problem?

✓ What is the major reason for "Recognizing and identifying symptoms?"

✓ What happens to the problem of alcohol and drug addiction when you devote time and effort to its symptoms?

✓ The book states that "You cannot solve a problem just by treating its symptoms only." Please explain the meaning of this statement in the context of your past efforts to solve the addiction problem?

✓ The book states that "There are many red flags along the road to becoming an alcoholic and drug addict. You often ignored these danger warning signs on your way to the bottom. What were your red flags?

What is the Problem? Stop Focusing on the Symptoms (HTSS PGS. 35-36)

In order to identify the real problem, you have to ask the question, "Do I have a problem"?

Other addicts pointed out that they believed the real problem to be a combination of the following: drinking too much, limiting the number of drinks, drinking alone at home, drinking first thing in the morning, having too much alcohol in the fridge at home, or switching from whisky to wine.

- ✓ Which of these misunderstandings of the real problem have you used when you were doing alcohol and drugs?

- ✓ How well did these efforts work for you?

- ✓ What is the meaning of the following statement, "There is no right way of doing the wrong thing."
- ✓ How many substance abuse treatment programs did you attend in the past and how long did you stay sober after leaving the program?

- ✓ What helped you to stay sober for that long?

- ✓ What caused you to relapse after being sober for some time?

The Phenomenon of Craving (HTSS PGS. 36-38)

The book states that "The first drink always triggers the physical desire for subsequent drinks."

- ✓ Describe your typical behavior pattern after the first drink on any given day?
- ✓ Explain the meaning of the following statement "You use your rational mind to take the first drink."
- ✓ What happens to your mind and body as the number of drinks increase?
- ✓ Explain why "One or two drinks are never enough."
- ✓ Explain the meaning of this phrase "bodily physical cravings for more alcohol?"
- ✓ Why does an alcoholic/drug user often drink and use more than intended or originally budgeted for?
- ✓ According to the book, why is there a difference between drinking alcohol and consuming other drinks such as water, tea, coffee, or soda?"
- ✓ What are cravings according to the book?
- ✓ What is the phenomenon of craving according to the book?
- ✓ Explain why "The first drink is the culprit?"

Normal vs Abnormal Drinkers (HTSS PGS. 38-40)

- ✓ What are the two types of alcohol users? And which one did you think you were when you were using?

✓ Why are normal drinkers able to stop after a few?
✓ People who use pills often cut them into pieces so that they can last longer. Why is this kind of behavior a form of self-deception?
✓ Explain the following statement "Abnormal drinkers are allergic to alcohol?"
✓ Describe the role of the body and the mind during the process of getting drunk?
✓ According to the book, why do "people drink until they pass out?"
✓ How did you feel and behave the morning after a night of drinking and or using drugs? What did you say to yourself?
✓ Explain the following phrase "The negative after-effects of alcohol and drugs?"

Mental Obsession (HTSS PGS. 40-41)

✓ What made you decide to quit using alcohol or drugs in the past?
✓ How long were you sober on each occasion that you decided to quit?
✓ What caused you to go back to doing alcohol and drugs after you have been sober for some time? (Highlight your thoughts and feelings just before you got drunk or high again).
✓ How well did you handle the negative emotions of being "restless, discontent, irritable, frustration" during your brief sober period?
✓ According to the book, what tends to happen when "You may fight and resist the temptation to drink?"
✓ What is a mental obsession, and what causes it to become more intense and uncontrollable?

Admit the Problem (HTSS PGS. 41-43)

✓ What is to admit the problem?
✓ Why is it important to admit the problem? And what difference does it make?
✓ List some of the things that you have admitted pertaining to alcohol and drug abuse?
✓ You knew what is right and wrong during your addiction days. What were some of the right things, choices or actions that you ignored in favor of doing what you knew to be wrong?
✓ Why is admitting "powerlessness the real beginning of the recovery process?"
✓ What are the four different ways of admitting as listed in the book?
✓ How were you delusional when doing alcohol and drugs?
✓ Explain the following statement "your motives to drink and do drugs were driven by insanity, and that your beliefs about alcohol and drugs were insane too?"
✓ What were some of the lies you told yourself when you were using? (Examples are ("I can quit anytime." "I can have a few and stop.")

Admit the Problem is Powerlessness Over Alcohol or Drugs and not Something Else (HTSS PGS. 43-44)

What is powerlessness over alcohol/drugs, and what causes it?

Answer: Powerlessness is the inability to control or stop drinking after taking the first drink. This is caused by the body craving for more even after you told yourself that you will have a few and stop. It is the vicious cycle where you want to stop but cannot due to the craving in the body (not in your mind) triggered by the first drink.

The conclusion is that "You are powerless over alcohol" because of the craving and the mental obsession. You want to quit but cannot due to mental obsession. The combination of bodily craving and mental obsession are the factors that make you powerless over alcohol.

Module C Thought Starters
Introduction to Module C - (HTSS PGS. 45-46)

Thought starters in this 3rd module are designed to concentrate on the major consequences of powerlessness in the life of the alcoholic and drug addict.

- ✓ What is the meaning of the phrase that "life became increasingly unmanageable?"
- ✓ What is the difference between good and bad management according to the book?

Life Being Unmanageable (HTSS PGS. 16-22)

- ✓ Give five examples of specific symptoms of powerlessness that you experienced while doing alcohol and drugs in each of the following aspects of your life?

- ✓ **Your Physical Health**: In what specific ways was your "Physical Health" unmanageable because of powerlessness over alcohol and drugs?

- ✓ **Your Mental Health**: In what specific ways was your "Mental Health" unmanageable because of powerlessness over alcohol and drugs?

- ✓ **Your Spiritual Health**: In what specific ways was your "Spiritual Health" unmanageable because of powerlessness over alcohol and drugs?

- ✓ **Your Financial Life**: In what specific ways was your "Financial Life" unmanageable because of powerlessness over alcohol and drugs?

- ✓ **Relationship With Yourself:** In what specific ways was your "Relationship With Yourself" unmanageable because of powerlessness over alcohol and drugs?

- ✓ **Relationship With Your Family and Friends**: In what specific ways was your

"Relationship with Your Family and Friends" unmanageable because of powerlessness over alcohol and drugs?

✓ **Your Marriage(s):** In what specific ways was your "Marriage Relationship" unmanageable because of powerlessness over alcohol and drugs?

✓ **Lost Love, Respect and Trust**: You lost the love, respect and trust of your loved ones while drinking and doing drugs. List some of the specific things you did to lose their love, respect and trust?

✓ **Rebuilding Broken Relationships:** Being sober is very important in your recovery work, but sobriety alone is not enough. There is a need to repair damaged relationships with the people in your life. It is essential that you work toward regaining the love and trust that you lost due to alcohol and a self-centered lifestyle. What specific things are you going to do to regain the love, trust, and respect of your loved ones?

✓ **Your Work/Job-Career Life:** How was your work impacted by your alcohol/ drug use? In what specific ways was your "Work/Job-Career" unmanageable because of powerlessness over alcohol and drugs?

✓ **Your Legal Life**: In what specific ways was your "Legal Life" unmanageable because of powerlessness over alcohol and drugs?

✓ **Your Transportation Status:** In what specific ways was your "Transportation Status" unmanageable because of powerlessness over alcohol and drugs?

✓ **Your Housing Situation:** In what specific ways was your "Housing Status" unmanageable because of powerlessness over alcohol and drugs?

✓ **Your Hobbies:** What hobbies did you engage in when you were doing alcohol and drugs?

✓ **How did you spend your spare time?** How often did you go on vacation and which vacation places did you visit? In what specific ways were your "Hobbies" unmanageable because of powerlessness over alcohol and drugs?

Importance and Benefits of Admitting Powerlessness (HTSS PGS. 68-70)

The major goal of this lesson is for the participants to appreciate all the self- analysis work they have done so far in all the previous lessons which should have persuaded them to admit that there is a real problem, not an imaginary one, which needs your attention. In the past, most addicts admitted there was some problem without clarity on what the problem was and no clue on how to make the problem go away. This admission should emphasize the following points:

✓ You are admitting that the problem of powerlessness has been there for a long time.

- ✓ To admit is to finally surrender, no more denial, no more pretense, no more blaming, no more excuses, and no more fabricated justifications.

- ✓ To admit is to stop fighting the disease, to stop resisting, to give up, and to give in.

- ✓ It is to accept that a problem exists which is more powerful than your limited five senses; and, therefore, cannot solve it by yourself without the aid of a greater power.

- ✓ To admit is to yield to the reality that self has failed, your own efforts are not working, and that you need something greater and more powerful than yourself.

- ✓ Admission is taking responsibility for your beliefs, choices and actions.

- ✓ Admitting brings you to a position where you emphatically decide that you cannot continue the same way; you are coming up clean and opening up to the reality which has always been there.

- ✓ To admit is to acknowledge the presence of a problem whose existence you denied for a long time.

- ✓ You are finally conceding to the fact that all along, you were a slave to alcohol, it has become your master, and it has taken control over your life.

- ✓ You are practically demonstrating that you now know that you have not been in charge, alcohol was, and if you continue to drink, you will also continue to be a servant to alcohol.

- ✓ To admit is to surrender defeat, to throw in the towel.

What have you admitted?

This part of instruction is to emphasize the importance of admitting, especially some issues which were taken for granted by the alcoholic and drug addict. If these issues are not admitted, they may come back to haunt the addict and slow down sobriety progress. Here are examples of some specific issues to be admitted: (HTSS PGS. 68-70)

- ✓ Admitting that you pushed away loved ones and let them down again and again.

- ✓ That you were being dishonesty to think that you were in control when in reality alcohol was.

- ✓ That you continued going in the wrong direction with both eyes open.

- ✓ That you knew something was wrong but did very little to nothing about it.

- ✓ Drinking and encountering problems but kept going deceiving yourself that

✓ it will get better.

✓ Hurting yourself and others but remained convinced that drinking harmed nobody.
✓ You are admitting that alcohol and drugs were more important than paying bills, buying food, and spending quality time with family.

✓ You are admitting that you have a problem that you didn't know how to handle or do something about.

✓ That you were imprisoned and hospitalized by alcohol while walking around the streets.

✓ That you liked being high or drunk but ignored the consequences.

✓ That you used anger to silence people and get what you want, force your way through self-engineered predicaments and sometimes to hide the pain inside.

✓ That you are no longer willing to invest your time and money in your own downfall.

✓ By admitting you are commanding yourself to stop scoring your own goals and stop opposing yourself.

Question:

What is the good news that comes with genuinely and sincerely admitting powerlessness over alcohol/drugs?

Module D Thought Starters
What Is the Solution to Powerlessness?

Why are the following not good solutions to the problem of alcohol and drug addiction: "Moving to another city," "changing from whisky to wine," and "drinking after working hours or weekends only?"

What are beliefs and where do they come from? (HTSS PG. 71)

✓ What is a belief?
✓ Where do beliefs come from?
✓ What were your beliefs about alcohol and drugs when you were doing it?

What is believing? (HTSS PG. 72)

✓ What are the four components of believing?
✓ Every person is a believer irrespective of whether you belong to a religious group. Do you agree or disagree and why?
✓ Explain the meaning of the following statement "Your beliefs can either work for you or against you."

✓ Describe how you came to treat alcohol/drugs as your God or Higher Power?

✓ What is the meaning of giving your power to alcohol and drugs?

Nature of Believing: Spiritual vs Physical (Non Spiritual) (HTSS PGS. 72-73)

✓ What is the difference between spiritual and sense knowledge based believing?

✓ Why is spiritual believing more powerful than depending on your five senses only?

✓ Explain the meaning of the following statement "the solution to powerlessness and therefore, your addiction problem is not in what you already know but in what you come to believe."

✓ Explain the meaning of the following and what it means to you," Spiritual believing requires you to see the invisible, believe the unbelievable, expect the unexpected, experience and witness the impossible, trust the unknown."

Believing In a Greater Power (HTSS PGS. 73-75)

✓ Why is Higher Power considered to be higher and greater?

✓ What were some of your beliefs about alcohol and drugs when you were using?

✓ Your beliefs should work for you and not against you. How well did those beliefs in # 2 above work for you?

✓ What is the connection between believing and thinking?

✓ What is the connection between thinking and feelings?

✓ Explain the meaning of the following statement "When you are going through difficult life situations you want help from a source that is able to deliver you and rescue you all the time and not sometimes."

✓ What do the following phrases mean "rely on what is unreliable, depend on what is undependable, and trust on what is untrustworthy?" Give your answer in the context of your alcohol/drug using days.

✓ What are the characteristics and abilities of alcohol and drugs that attracted you to rely, depend and trust in them?

✓ What are the "characteristics and abilities of God or Higher Power that you can avail yourself to in order to solve the problem of powerlessness?"

✓ What are the advantages of your Higher Power/God being available to you 24/7?

Predominant and Recurrent Thought Patterns of the Alcohol and Drug Abuser (HTSS PGS. 75-79)

✓ Why did you keep on using when doing so was no longer fun nor enjoyable?

✓ Make a detailed list of your predominant beliefs about alcohol and drugs that you were usually preoccupied with while using?

✓ Explain the meaning of the following statement "Your predominant and recurrent belief patterns helped to make you sink deeper and deeper into alcoholism and drug addiction."

✓ Explain the meaning of the following statement "Addiction beliefs are always alive and active until they are removed and replaced by new ones."

✓ Explain the meaning of the following statement "Alcohol and drugs worked so well because you had unwavering strong faith in them."

Paradigm Shift (HTSS PG. 79)

- ✓ Why do some alcoholics and drug addicts get surprised and "shocked when they relapse?"
- ✓ Explain why "old and new beliefs cannot exist together in harmony?"
- ✓ What is a paradigm?
- ✓ Explain the meaning of the following statement "As a person grows older, 95% of who you are is in a set of memorized programs."

Emotional Addictions (HTSS PGS. 80-81)

- ✓ What are memorized emotions?
- ✓ Give at least five examples drawn from your own experience?
- ✓ What are the effects of "thinking and feeling the same negative way over many years?"
- ✓ Explain the meaning of the following statement "using past events in your life to validate and justify your memorized negative emotions that have become part of who you are."
- ✓ Explain the meaning of the following statement "It is almost impossible to solve your problems while you continue to live by emotions of the past."
- ✓ Explain the meaning of the following statements "You will begin to argue for your limitations and find excuses for not changing. In short, the framework of mind that created alcohol addiction cannot help you to be sober."
- ✓ What are the three key skills needed for you to change effectively?

Your Case Histories: Participants should do this exercise following the examples given in the book: (HTSS PGS. 81-83)

Practical Exercise 3
Your Old Beliefs--- Write Your Story

Question:

What did you think, feel and believe about alcohol and drugs when you were using?

Practical Exercise 4
Your New Beliefs -- Write Your Story

Question:

What should you think and believe about alcohol and drugs now that you want to be clean and sober?

Mind-Body Connection (HTSS PGS. 83-85)

- ✓ How is the mind connected to the body and spirit?
- ✓ Describe the process of what happens every time you have a thought?
- ✓ Why is it important to fully understand the process you described in the question above?
- ✓ What are the consequences of having most of your of thoughts, decisions, choices and actions based on your feelings?
- ✓ How much rational thinking did you put into drinking alcohol and using drugs?
- ✓ Explain the meaning of the following statement. "The body should be a servant to the mind, but when you think based on how you feel, the mind becomes the servant to the body."
- ✓ Discuss the following questions "How many times did you drive and got home safely but could not remember how you got home? Who drove you home on those occasions when you blacked out while sitting behind the wheel?"
- ✓ Explain the meaning of the following statements "When mind and body are working in opposition, there can never be change especially when the body becomes the mind. Successful change demands that you think greater than how you feel, to think greater than the memorized emotions in the body."

Your Case Histories: Participants should do this exercise following the examples given in the book. (HTSS PGS. 85-89)

Practical Exercise 5
Your Old Beliefs-Write Your Story

Question:

What did you think, feel and believe about alcohol and drugs when you were using?

Practical Exercise 6
Your New Beliefs- Write Your Story

Question:

What should you think and believe about alcohol and drugs now that you want to be clean and sober?

- ✓ Explain the meaning of the following statement "Sobriety requires that you see the world in a new light. How you see the world when drinking cannot help you to stay sober."
- ✓ Explain the meaning of the following statement "You have to reprogram your mind by identifying habitual beliefs and thought patterns associated with drinking/drugs, bring them to the surface and then replace them with new ones that will help you to stay sober."
- ✓ What are your new thoughts and beliefs about alcohol and drugs now that you want to stay sober?

Practical Exercise 7

Your Predominant and Recurrent Thought Patterns While Using (HTSS PGS. 89-90)

- ✓ What were your predominant and recurrent thought patterns about alcohol and drugs while you were using?

In order to benefit from this exercise, be as specific and detailed as possible in coming up with your list. Your answers to this question will, among other things, help you to gain insight on why you continued to use even when it was no longer fun and exciting to do so.

Restore Us to Sanity (HTSS PGS. 90-95)

- ✓ What was your response when people expressed concern at your drinking or drug abuse? (Be honest).
- ✓ Most addicts believe that their situation is special, unique and not that bad. Describe your own view of being unique about doing alcohol and drugs?
- ✓ What is insanity?
- ✓ How were you insane when you were doing alcohol and drugs?

✓ Give five examples of the lies you told yourself, believed in and lived by?

Question:

Write two of your own stories showing specific ways of insanity while using alcohol and drugs?

Module E Thought Starters
Introduction to Module E (HTSS PG. 96)

✓ Explain the meaning of the following statement "you gave over your will and your life to the care of drugs and alcohol?"
✓ What is the meaning of "turning point" as contained in the following statement "This is a turning point where you have to make a clear decision about how you will live your life from this point forward?"
✓ What are the three choices available to you as you continue work on long-term sobriety? What is your preferred choice and why?

The Role of Self on Your Way to the Bottom (HTSS PGS. 97-100)

✓ What is self, and why do you have to give up self-will?
✓ How did self-will manifest itself when you were doing alcohol and drugs?
✓ List some of your choices and actions that were driven by selfishness, self-deception, fear, "resentment, self-seeking attitude and pressure for immediate self-gratification?"
✓ "Selfishness is lack of consideration for others". List examples of times when you behaved in selfish and inconsiderate ways?
✓ List examples of situations where you placed yourself "in a position to be hurt and be in conflict with yourself and others?"
✓ What was your justification for getting angry, indignant, resentful and blaming others when things didn't go your way even if it was the wrong way? How smart and wise are those justifications now that you want to be sober?
✓ What are the similarities and differences between being self-centered, self-seeking, and egocentric?
✓ Write a list of actions you knew to be wrong and inappropriate but did them, anyway?
✓ Explain the meaning of the following statements, "The fact that you have stopped drugs and alcohol does not automatically make you humble, honest, tolerant, and patient. If you have been selfish and self-centered for many years, these negative habits will not go away on their own. They will not disappear just because you have stopped drinking for a few days?"
✓ What are you going to do in order to gain the following desirable characteristics -- "humility, tolerance, patience, selflessness, and honesty?"

Question:

In what specific ways were you selfish, self-centered, and self-seeking when you were doing alcohol and drugs?

Describe specific incidents of the manifestation of self and self-will when you were doing alcohol and drugs?

What is decision-making?-Turning Point (HTSS PGS. 101-104)

- ✓ What is decision-making?
- ✓ How did you make decisions when you were using alcohol and drugs?
- ✓ How was the quality of those decisions?
- ✓ How sound were your daily decisions to do alcohol and drugs?
- ✓ What facts or considerations were those decisions based on?
- ✓ How proud and satisfied are you about those decisions then and now?
- ✓ How smart and wise do you look?
- ✓ "The problem of alcoholism is powerlessness, and the solution is believing in a greater power. Question: (You were trying to get power from alcohol and drugs, temporary fix). Where are you going to get the power that will enable you to stay sober?
- ✓ The book states that "Sound decisions are based on facts. Daily decisions to drink and use drugs tended to ignore the facts which led to undesirable results and regrets." List eight facts that you have gathered about the addiction problem from your work so far in this program.
- ✓ What is the appropriate conclusion you should make based on the assembled facts?
- ✓ What exactly do you do when turning over your will and your life to God?

What is your will and your life? (HTSS PGS. 104-105)

- ✓ What is self-will?
- ✓ How do you benefit "from yielding to a greater power than trying to do recovery your own way?"
- ✓ List specific examples of "self-defeating and self-destructive belief patterns" that you used to entertain?

Who are you turning it over to? Who are you surrendering to? (Spirituality vs Religion) (HTSS PGS. 105-107)

- ✓ How do you feel about letting go off habits that you have been practicing for so many years?
- ✓ How do you feel about allowing someone or something to exercise control over your life? (Remember that you used to allow alcohol and drugs to control you).
- ✓ What is the difference between spirituality and religion?
- ✓ In what specific ways did you surrender your life to alcohol and drugs?
- ✓ What were the qualities of alcohol and drugs that compelled you to turn over your will and your life to them?
- ✓ What exactly are you doing when you are surrendering your life to Higher Power/God?
- ✓ What are the qualities of God that should motivate you turn over your will and your life to Him day after day?
- ✓ What exactly do you turn over to God/Higher Power (shortcomings/ character defects) and what do you get back in return?

Why surrendering to God-Higher Power is important? (HTSS PGS. 107-114)

- ✓ Explain the meaning of the following statement "The same mind that created a problem cannot solve the problem?"
- ✓ What did you do to stay hooked and connected to alcohol and drugs?
- ✓ What can you do to stay hooked and connected to God instead of alcohol and drugs?
- ✓ According to the book, what is the major source of your "limitations and hardships"?
- ✓ According to the book, how does a person live in the past knowingly or unknowingly?
- ✓ How much longer are you going to continue tolerating being a slave to alcohol/drugs?
- ✓ How much longer are you going to continue tolerating alcohol/drugs being your masters/your bosses?
- ✓ According to the book, what is the major cause of relapse? (Correct answer is "hoping that their determination, thinking the same way, believing the same way will one day rescue them from their drinking troubles."
- ✓ What do the following phrases mean "get out of your own way", "stop obstructing God" and "quit impeding God's work in your life?"
- ✓ List the different ways that you can obstruct God?
- ✓ How did you demonstrate your trust and obedience to alcohol and drugs?
- ✓ What is the meaning of the following phrase "Let go and let God"?
- ✓ What is the meaning of the following phrase "anticipation prior to manifestation"?
- ✓ What does doubt, fear, frustration, worry and impatience indicate about your relationship with God/Higher Power? (Remember that you were always sure, dedicated and committed to alcohol and drugs).
- ✓ You were ready, willing and obedient to be led or guided by alcohol and drugs, what can you do so that you become ready, willing and obedient to
- ✓ be guided by God/Higher Power?
- ✓ You got daily instructions from alcohol and drugs when you were using. What are you going to do now so as to get daily instructions from a more reliable and dependable source; your Higher Power?

Self-Will Has Failed. Self-Will Did Not Work (HTSS PGS. 114-116)

- ✓ How much time do you have to continue failing by applying self-will?
- ✓ Explain the meaning of the following statements, "Alcoholics and drug addicts are in the habit of surrendering their self-will at the start of the day, then unknowingly take it back during the rest of the day.
- ✓ An addict may pray and even cry for help from God but quickly goes back to familiar negative habits?"
- ✓ Explain the meaning of the following statements "You had no doubts with alcohol and drugs. You had absolute trust in them but are fearful and hesitant with your Higher Power?"
- ✓ Explain the meaning of the following statement "Quit trying to be your own

higher power?"
- ✓ Explain the meaning of the following statement, "However, this time, your thinking, believing, and perceptions are directed by your Higher Power/God instead of being propelled by alcohol and drugs?"
- ✓ Explain the meaning of the following statement, "This type of change demands a shifting from being under the influence of alcohol to being under the inspiration and leadership of your Higher Power/God?"

How to become under the influence and direction of your Higher Power/God (HTSS PGS. 116-117)

Here we examine the difference between being under the influence of alcohol vs under the inspiration of God:

- ✓ You are familiar with being under the influence of alcohol and drugs.
- ✓ How do you get under the influence of Higher Power/God?
- ✓ Some people in recovery vehemently dislike and object to the idea of giving control over to a Higher Power, who is invisible and unfamiliar. To such people, Higher Power control is hard, impractical, very difficult and sometimes just not acceptable. They may have the following questions:

  - ➤ Who is Higher Power/God to you? (Remember who alcohol/drugs were to you?)

  - ➤ How do you contact and connect with an invisible power? (Remember how you stayed connected to alcohol and drugs).

  - ➤ How do you work with a power you do not see with your physical eyes?

  - ➤ How do you know if God/Higher Power is real? (Remember how real /drugs were). (Hint—your imagination).

- ✓ Explain the meaning of the following statement, "Due to inability to answer the above questions, some alcoholics continue using their self-will and own effort hoping for a different result."
- ✓ Alcohol as your higher power: The reality is that every alcoholic and drug addict has already surrendered his power, authority, independence, and freedom to alcohol and drugs. Check the list on (HTSS PGS. 117 -119).
- ✓ (The Addict Turned His Will and Life to Alcohol). Your task is to write a list of specific things you are going to do so as to be under the influence, inspiration, and guidance of your Higher Power/God? What are the daily habits that you are going to follow and adhere to?
- ✓ Explain the meaning of the following statement. "Denial, excuses, blaming, and justification do not take away the fact that you have lost control to alcohol and drugs."

How to establish a relationship with God-Higher Power (HTSS PGS. 120-125)

- ✓ What are the major ingredients of successful relationships?
- ✓ The book has examples of how some people viewed their relationship with alcohol and drugs under the following attributes: Trust, Commitment/ Loyalty, Respect, Active Listening and Paying Attention. Use the same four attributes to describe your ideal relationship with God/Higher Power?
- ✓ List the essential qualities of the God/Higher Power of your own understanding?

Action Planning For: Creating A Safe & Structured Recovery Environment -- Changing from Inside Out

This Action Planning exercise is about you creating a safe and structured environment for your long-term sobriety work. You had a structured environment for doing alcohol and drugs. It is important to put together a safe and structured recovery system consisting of daily routines and habits.

When you were using drugs and alcohol there was a pattern, a daily routine that evolved overtime, which you followed and adhered to. You perfected the system, and it always worked for you under every circumstance.

If you had a daily routine for drinking and doing drugs, what more now for your recovery? You also need such a daily routine for your recovery. You must be purposeful about how you are going to stay sober. You cannot afford to be vague, casual and thoughtless about your day if you are going to remain alcohol and drug free. Every person has 24 hours a day and your situation does not change that. Think about what you are going to do to stay sober today.

You knew exactly what to do, where to go and where to find your stuff. There was no hesitation or doubt in your mind about what you were going to do. You had a system and a daily ordered way of doing it. Your daily addiction habits and routines were very strong, very powerful, very energized and highly emotionally charged. You need a system and order for staying sober that is powerful, energized and highly emotionally charged. What are your new daily routines and intentions that will help you to stay sober?

The steps outlined below are designed to help you create a practical road map to staying sober.

You get back what you put in. Nothing for nothing. What do you think?

Your Safe & Structured Sobriety Plan

Please complete the steps outlined below and adhere to them as you continue working on being free from alcohol and drugs.

Step 1: Daily Habits

When you were drinking alcohol and doing drugs, you had daily habits, rituals, behaviors, actions, and routines that helped you to stay connected to the addiction lifestyle. Your task here is to list your new daily habits, rituals, behaviors, and routines that will help you to stay connected to a life free from alcohol and drugs.

1. _____

2. _____

3. _____

4. _____

5. _____

Step 2: Internal Mental Coping Skills

When you were using, you had specific beliefs, thought patterns, emotional states and mindset about alcohol and drugs which supported your continued consumption of these substances. Your task here is to list your new beliefs, new thoughts, new emotional states and new mindset about alcohol and drugs that will help you to stay sober? (Remember that you cannot stay sober on old beliefs and old thought patterns).

1. _____

2. _____

3. _____

Step 3: Support System

When you were drinking alcohol and doing drugs, you distanced yourself from people, places and things that were supportive of your wellbeing in preference of people, places and things that were detrimental to your welfare. Who are the people, places and things that will become part of your sobriety support system?

1. _____

2. _____

3. _____

4. _____

5. _____

Step 4: Your Time

When you were doing alcohol and drugs you spend most of your time preoccupied with either drinking and doing drugs or thinking and planning how, when, and where to get the next drink or drug. What are the new alternative alcohol and drug free ways to occupy your time in a meaningful and gainful manner? Your task here is to make a list of as many alcohol and drug free daily activities that you will engage in and that promote your sobriety?

1. _____

2. _____

3. _____

4. _____

5. _____

Step 5: Finances

When you were doing alcohol and drugs, you spend most of your money on alcohol and drugs. Your task here is to make a list of as many new alcohol and drug free ways of using your money that are beneficial to you and your loved ones?

1. _____

2. _____

3. _____

4. _____

5. _____

Step 6: Expectations

When you did alcohol and drugs you had certain expectations from your family members and friends? Now that you want to stay sober, what are your new expectations from your family members and friends? (Name them and your expectations from each one of them).

1. _____

2. _____

3. _____

4. _____

5. _____

Step 7: Family Relationships

When you were doing alcohol and drugs your family members and friends had certain expectations from you. What are the new expectations of your family members and friends from you? (Name each of them and their individual expectations from you).

1. _____

2. _____

3. _____

4. _____

5. _____

Resources

For more information on How to Stay Sober go to:

Sober At Last Online Academy is now offering How To Stay Sober (HTSS) program, follow this link-------------------

https://howtostaysobercom.wordpress.com/

https://soberatlast.thinkific.com/manage/courses/

https://www.jacksonvilletherapy.org/

Book link—bit.ly/HowToStaySoberBook

Workbook link bit.ly/StaySoberWorkbook

Contact Dr. Emmanuel Nzuzu—email nzumanu@yahoo.com

Printed in Great Britain
by Amazon

82164098R00047